KAKOOMA

ADDITION EDITION

Created by Greg Tang

SCHOLASTIC INC.
NEW YORK TORONTO LONDON AUCKLAND
SYDNEY MEXICO CITY NEW DELHI HONG KONG

TO GREG, EMILY, AND KATIE

Character design by Michaela Zanzani

Illustrated by Bill Alger

12 11 10 9 8 7 6 5 4 3 12 13 14 15 16

ISBN 978-0-545-46222-8
Printed in the U.S.A. 23
First printing, February 2012

TABLE OF CONTENTS

WHAT IS KAKOOMA?

Kakooma starts with a deceptively simple idea: In a group of numbers, find the number that is the sum of two others. Sounds easy, right? Sometimes it is, but other times the answer is right in front of you and you just can't see it. To solve a single puzzle, you often end up doing dozens of calculations in your head. Before you know it, your mind is sharper and your math skills are better. Kakooma makes you smarter.

WHO INVENTED KAKOOMA?

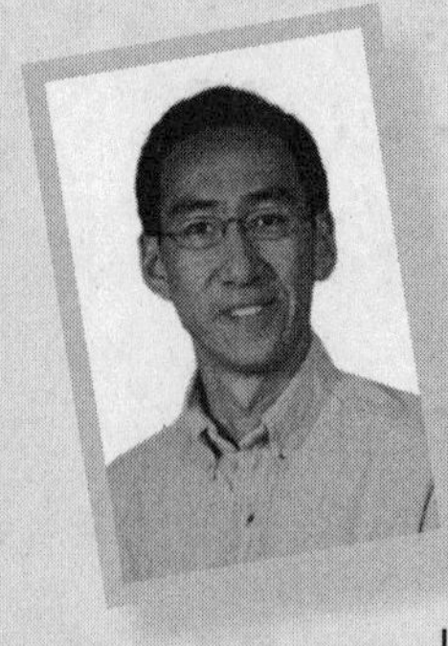

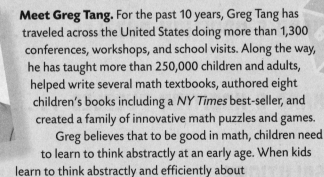

Meet Greg Tang. For the past 10 years, Greg Tang has traveled across the United States doing more than 1,300 conferences, workshops, and school visits. Along the way, he has taught more than 250,000 children and adults, helped write several math textbooks, authored eight children's books including a *NY Times* best-seller, and created a family of innovative math puzzles and games.

Greg believes that to be good in math, children need to learn to think abstractly at an early age. When kids learn to think abstractly and efficiently about numbers in groups rather than counting or memorizing, they can be taught common-sense strategies that make calculations fast and easy. Being able to connect and generalize these strategies across problems and operations is the key to thinking algebraically and the secret to being math smart.

HOW TO PLAY KAKOOMA

The Kakooma game board includes several different mini-puzzles (the diagram below shows six mini-puzzles with six numbers in each puzzle). In each mini-puzzle, there is only one number out of the six that is the sum of two others. Circle that number—that's your answer. Use all six answers to create the final "puzzle-in-a-puzzle" and solve that the same way.

Here's an example:

Choose a mini-puzzle to start with. Since 10 + 7 = 17, the answer is 17.

Next, look at the mini-puzzle to the right. Since 8 + 6 = 14, the answer is 14. Solve the four remaining mini-puzzles the same way and all six sums form . . . another puzzle!

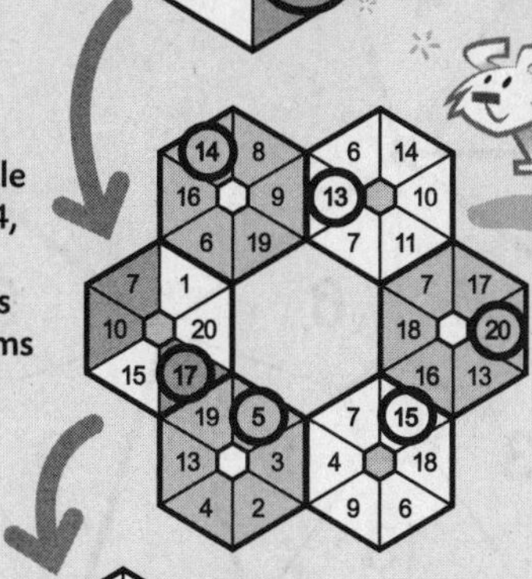

In this final puzzle, once again find the number that is the sum of two others. The final answer is 15 + 5 = 20.

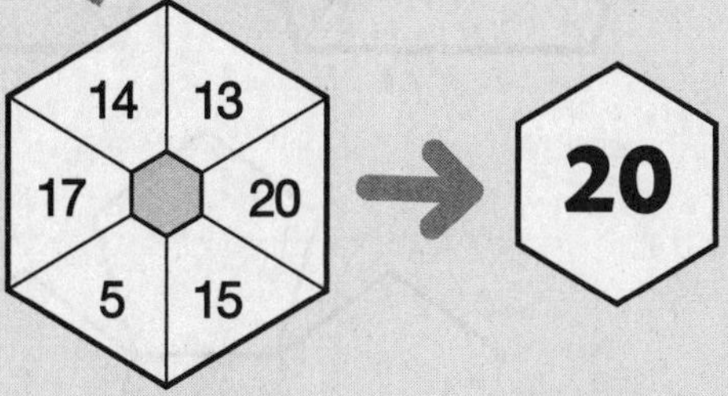

Difficulty levels The size of the puzzle and the size of the puzzle's numbers determine its difficulty. This book starts with the simplest "easy 5" puzzles and then progresses on to more difficult levels.

KAKOOMA EASY 5 ADDITION

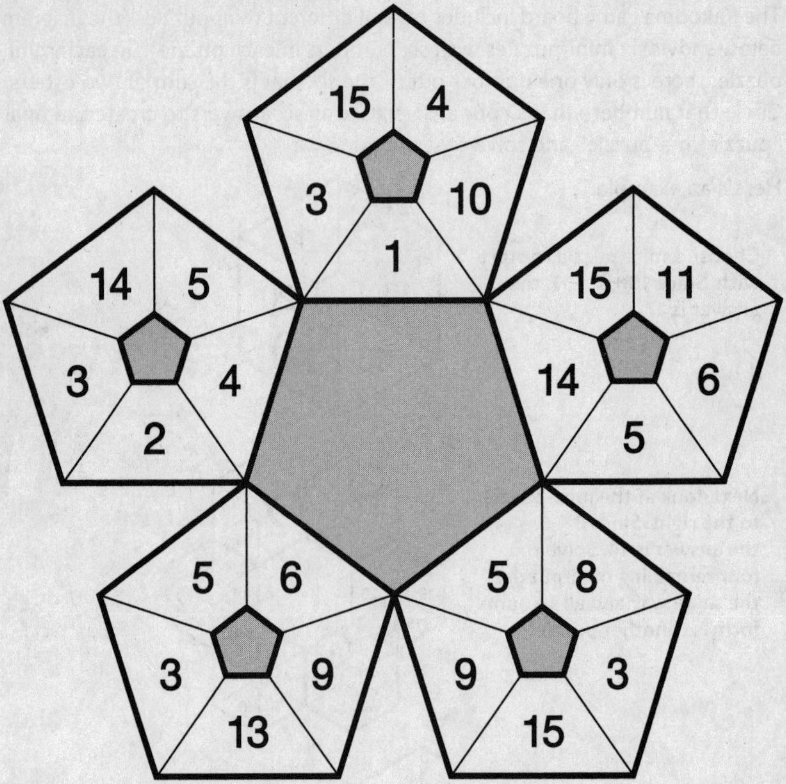

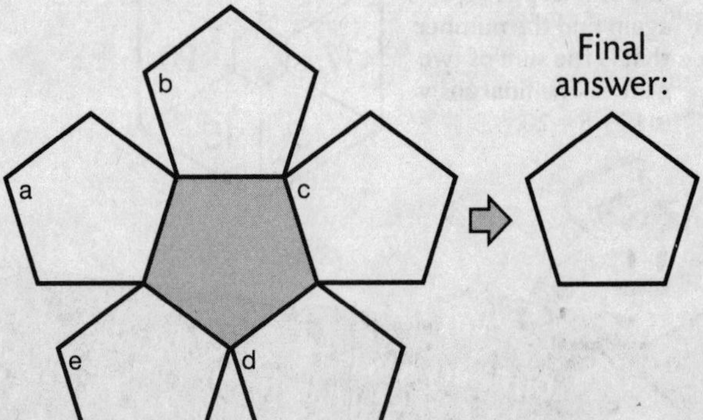

KAKOOMA EASY 5 ADDITION

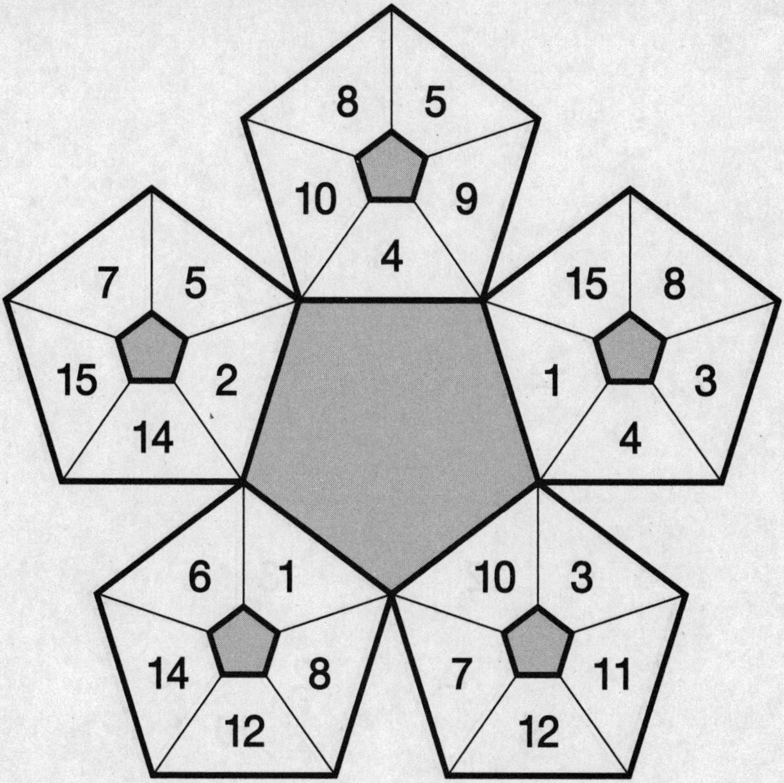

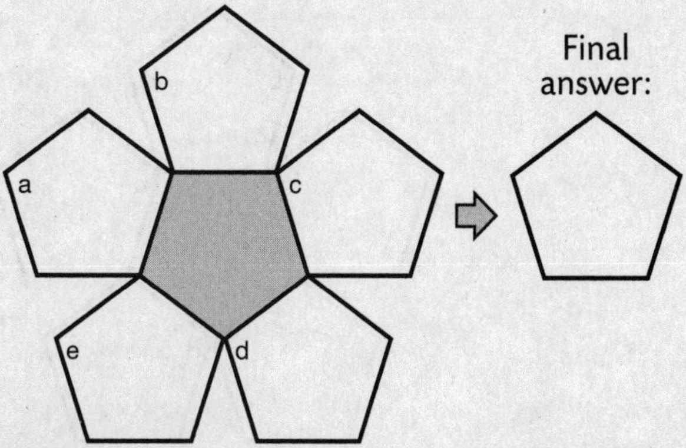

KAKOMA EASY 5 ADDITION

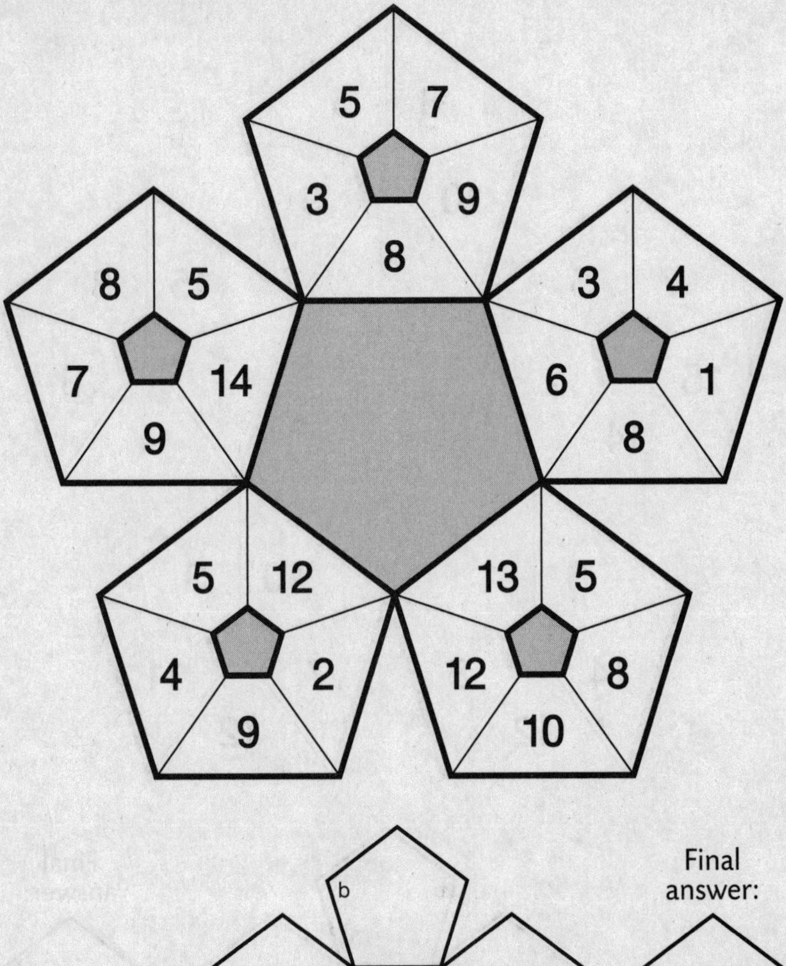

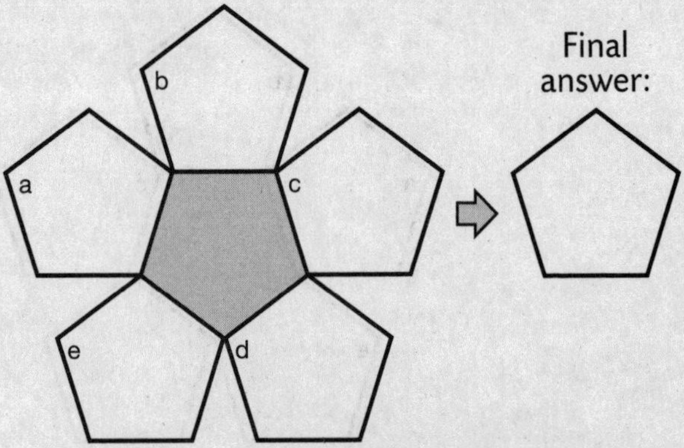

KAKOOMA EASY 5 ADDITION

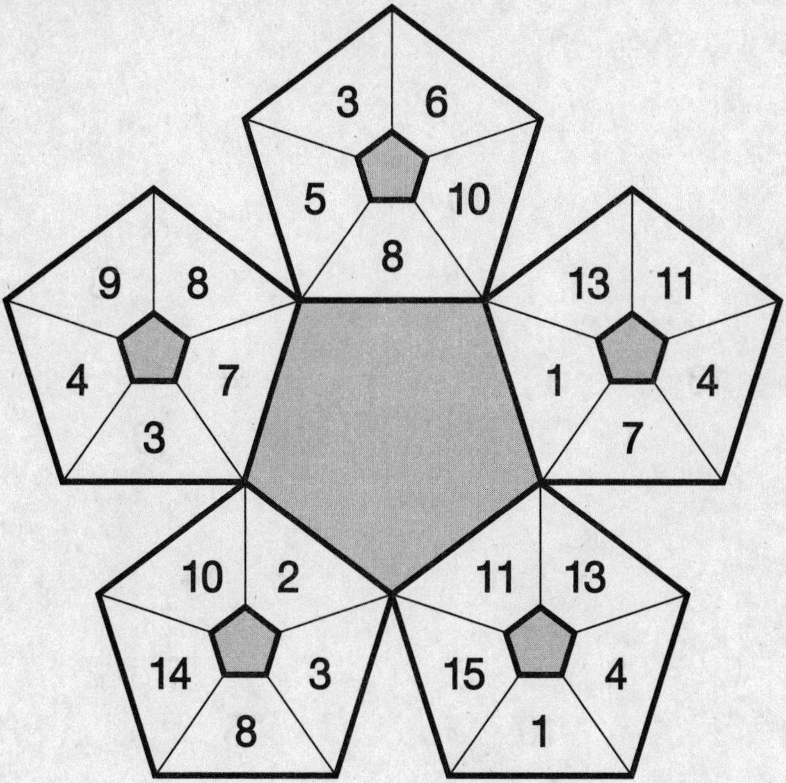

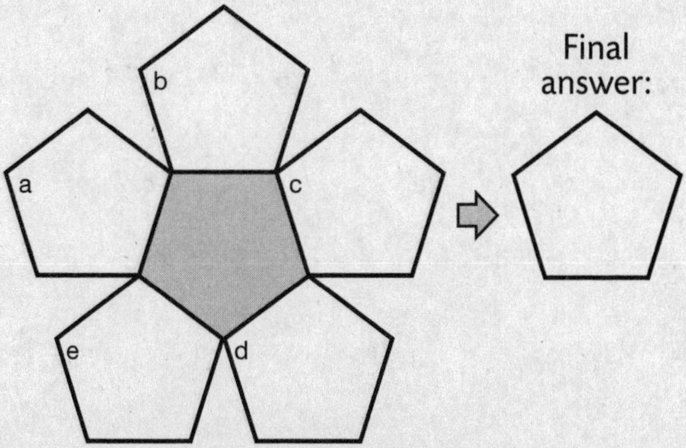

KAKOOMA EASY 5 ADDITION

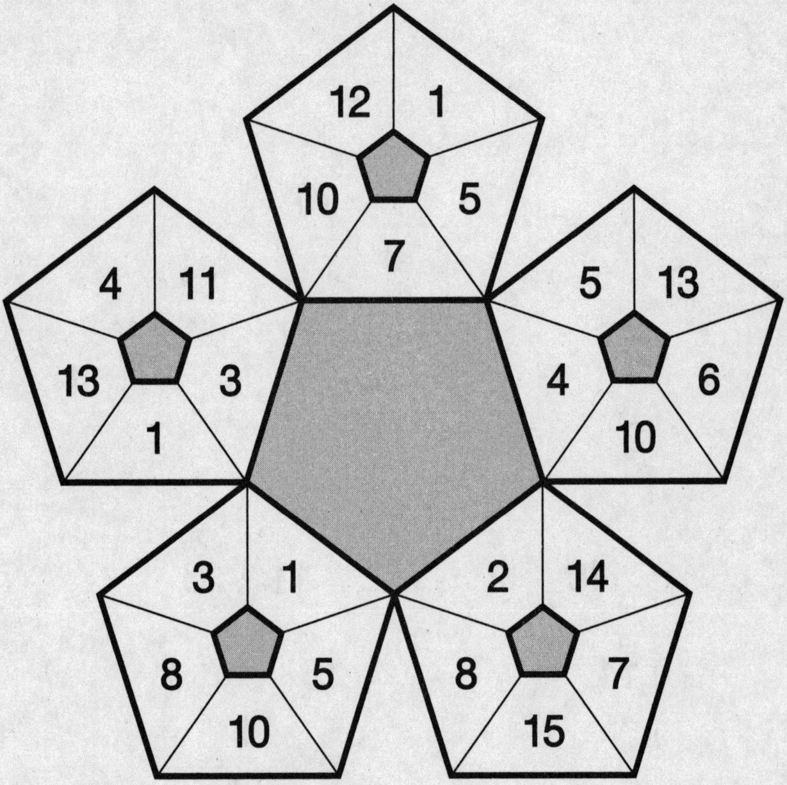

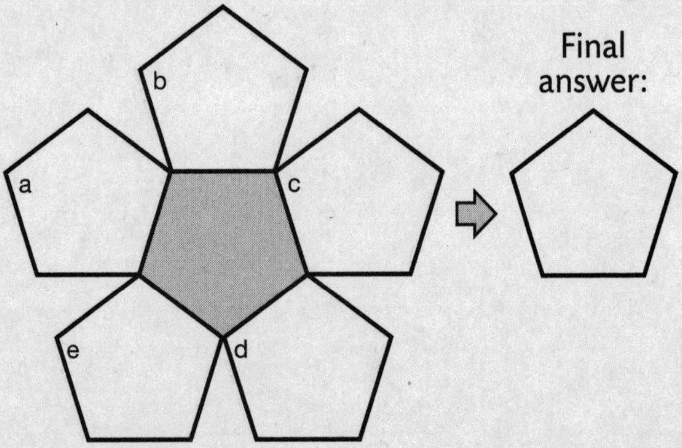

KAKOOMA EASY 5 ADDITION

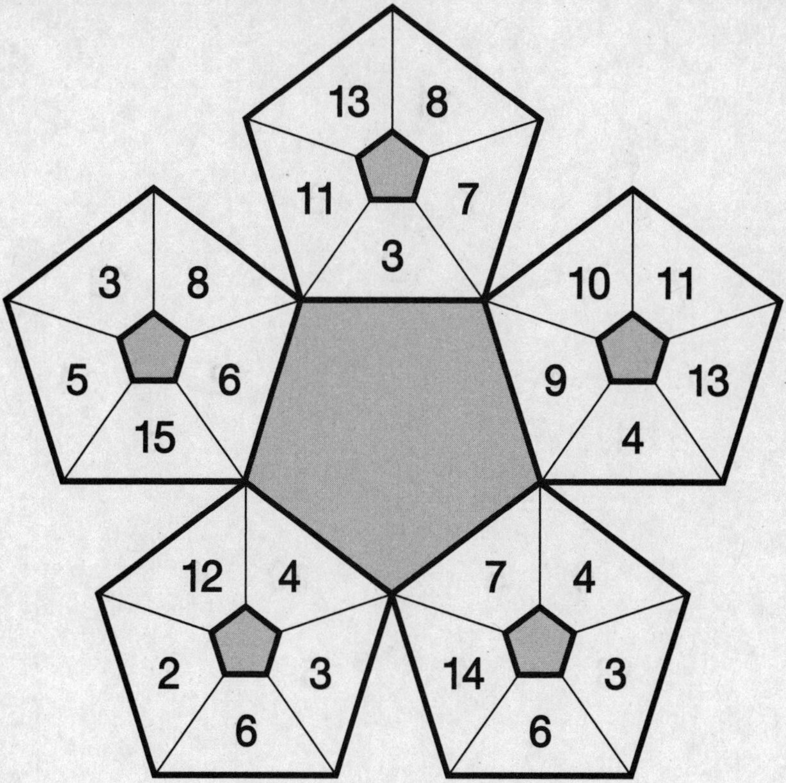

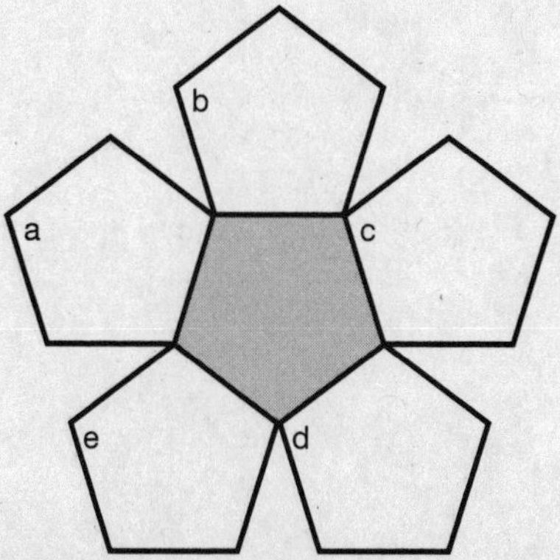

Final answer:

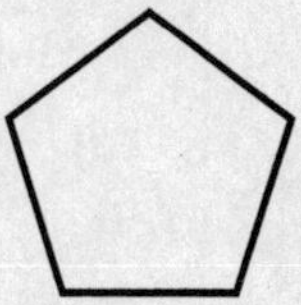

KAKOOMA EASY 5 ADDITION

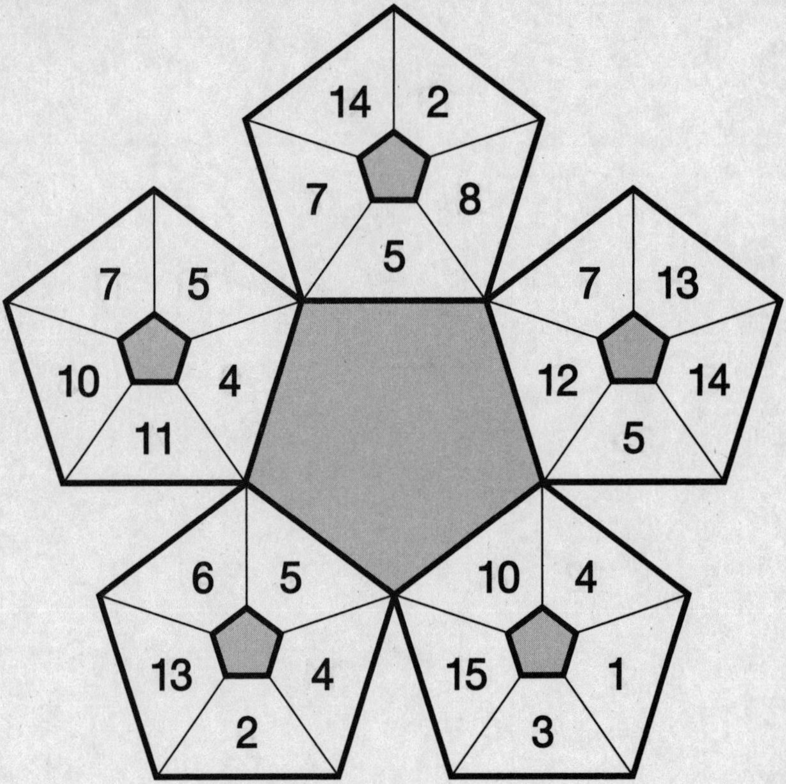

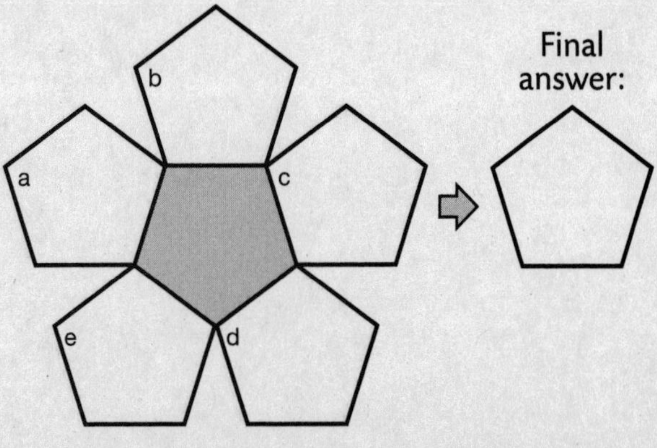

KAKOOMA EASY 5 ADDITION

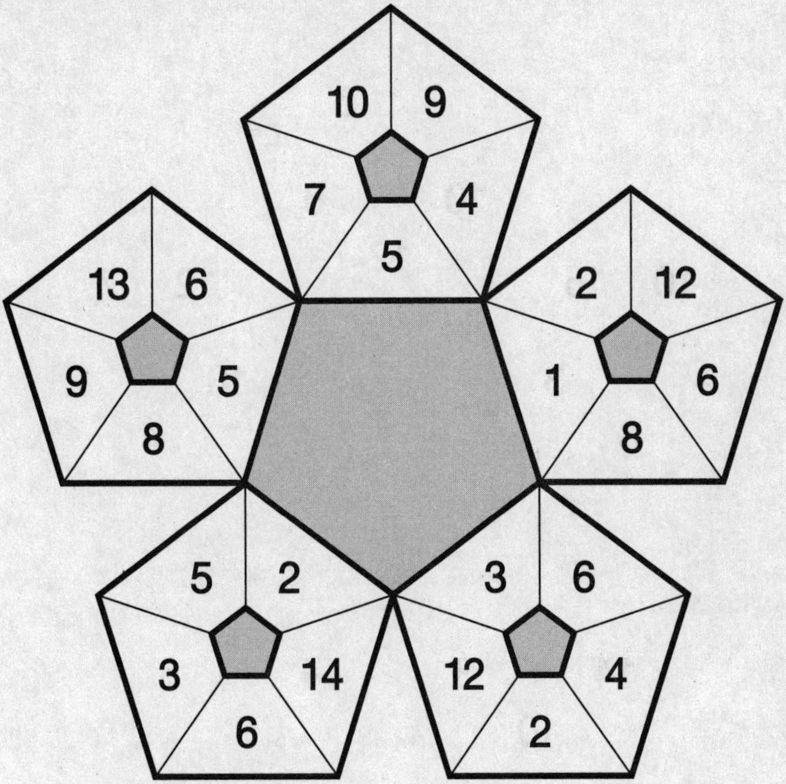

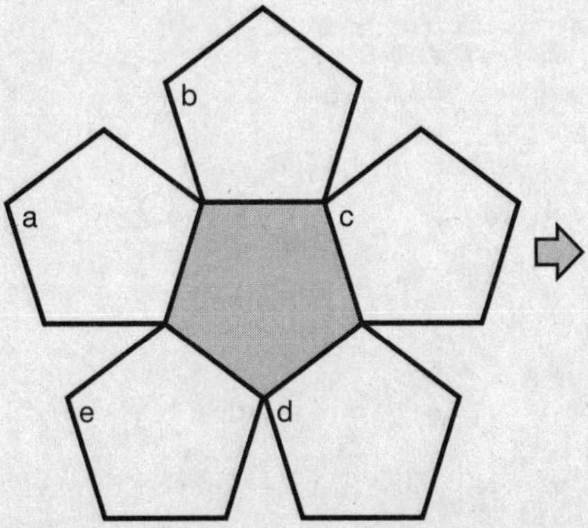

Final answer:

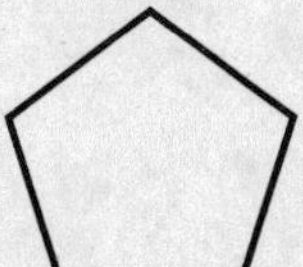

KAKOOMA EASY 5 ADDITION

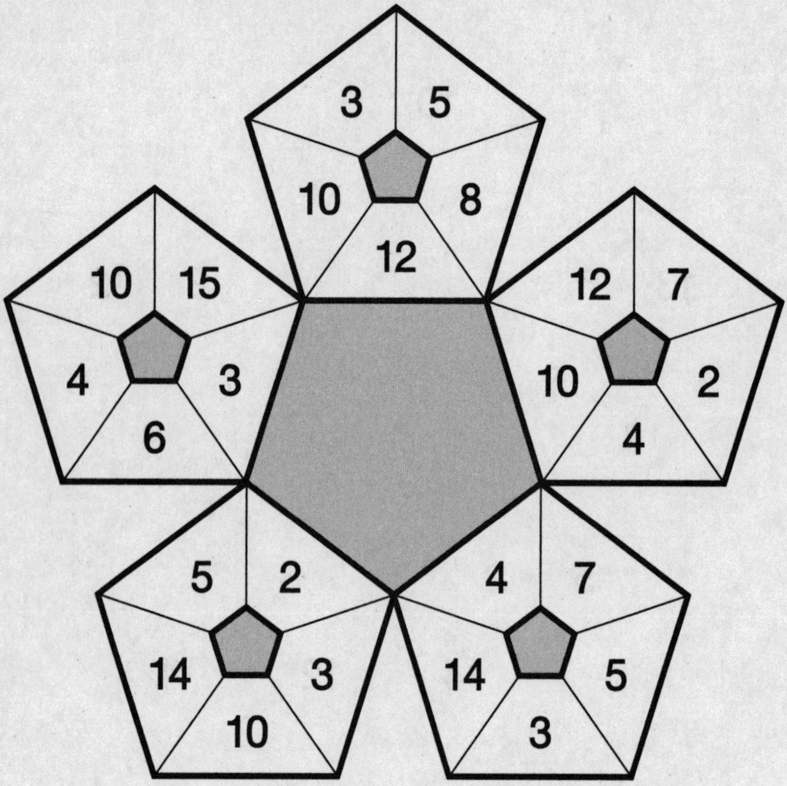

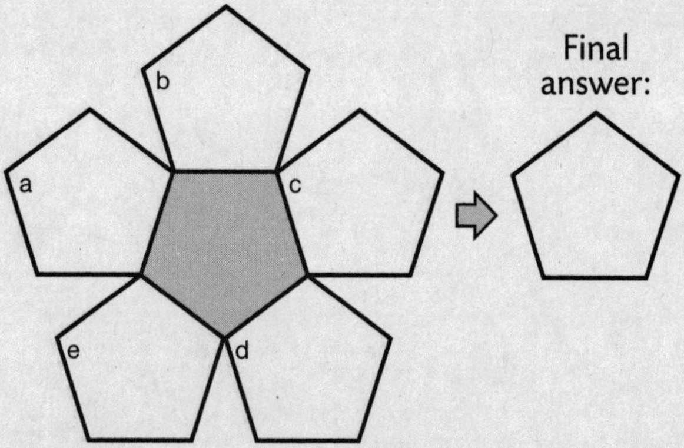

KAKOOMA EASY 5 ADDITION

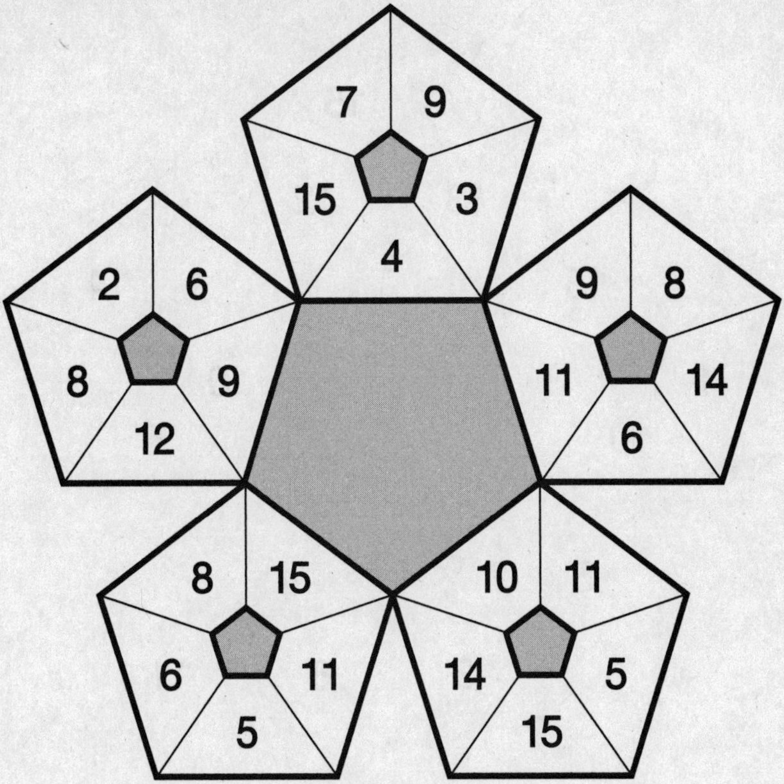

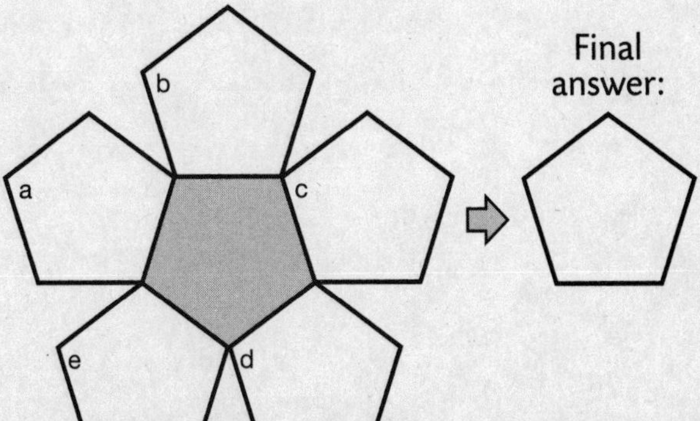

KAKOOMA EASY 5 ADDITION

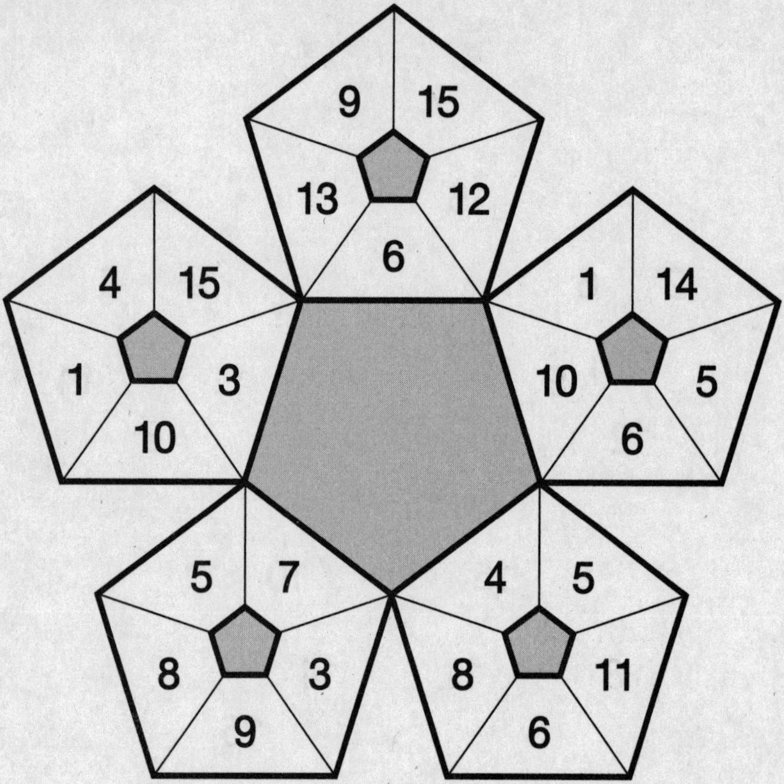

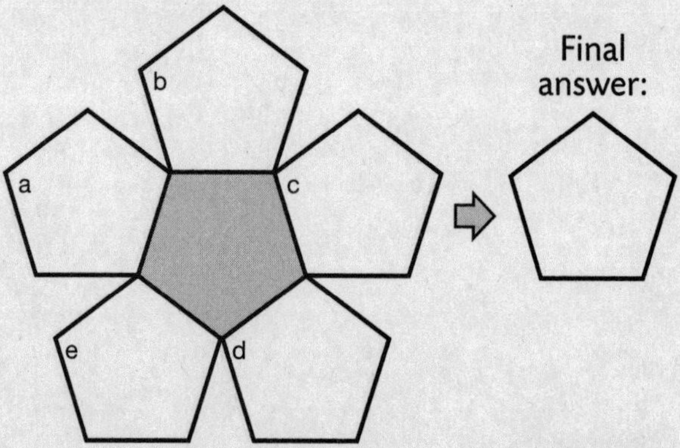

KAKOOMA EASY 5 ADDITION

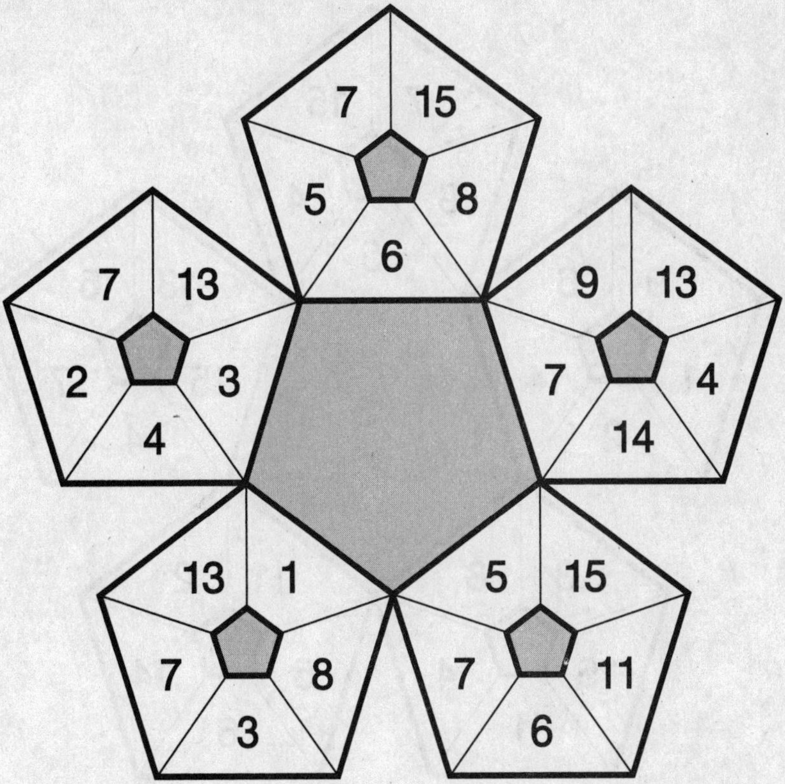

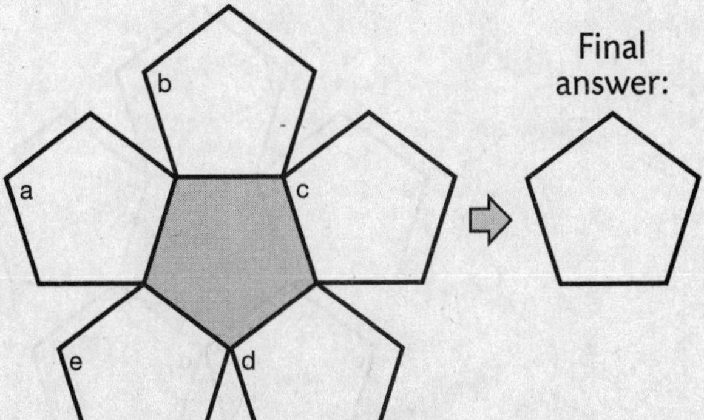

KAKOOMA EASY 5 ADDITION

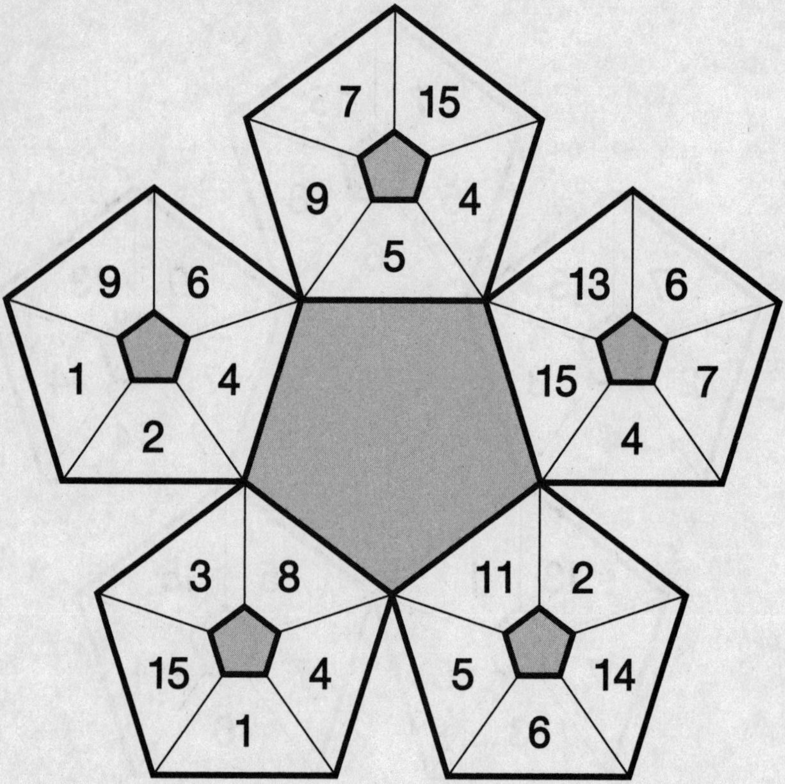

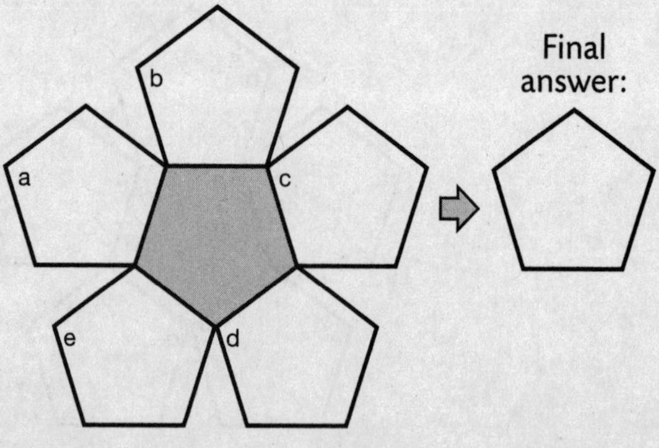

KAKOOMA EASY 5 ADDITION

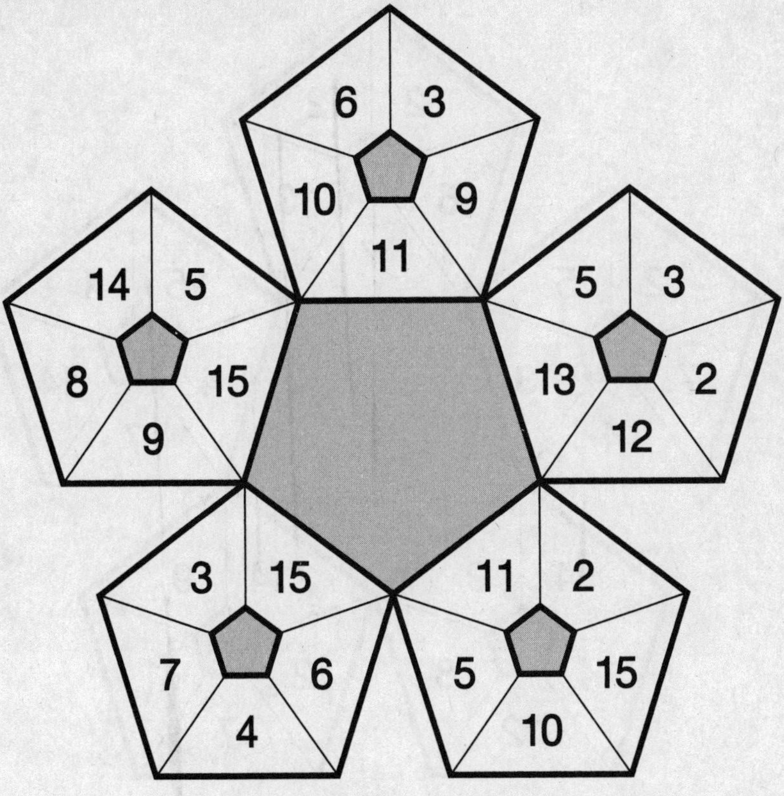

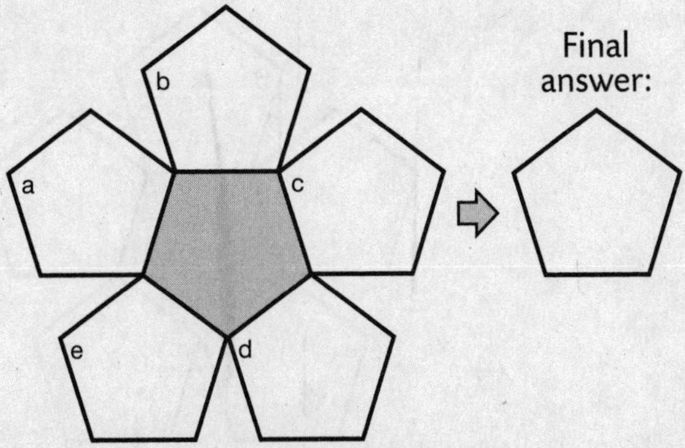

KAKOOMA EASY 5 ADDITION

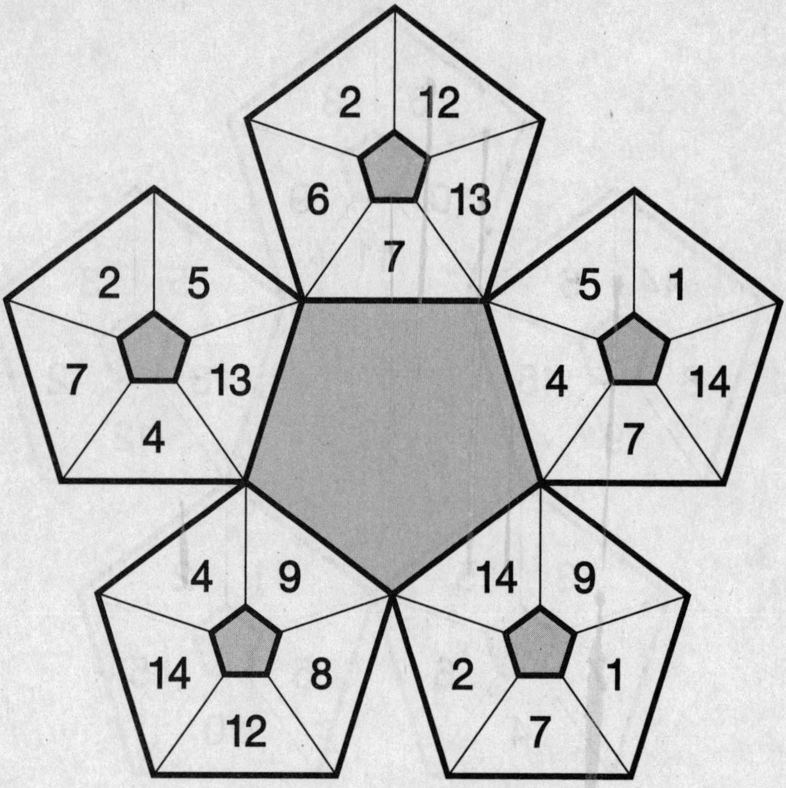

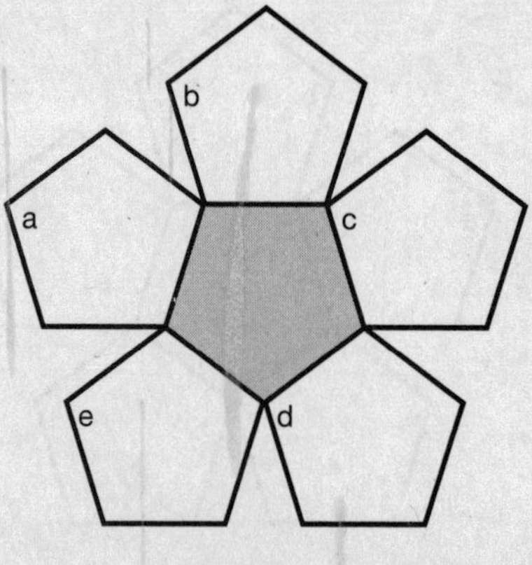

Final answer:

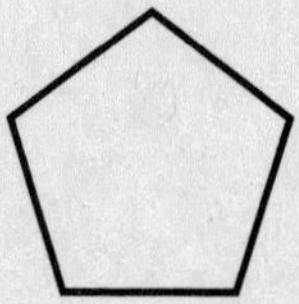

KAKOOMA EASY 6 ADDITION

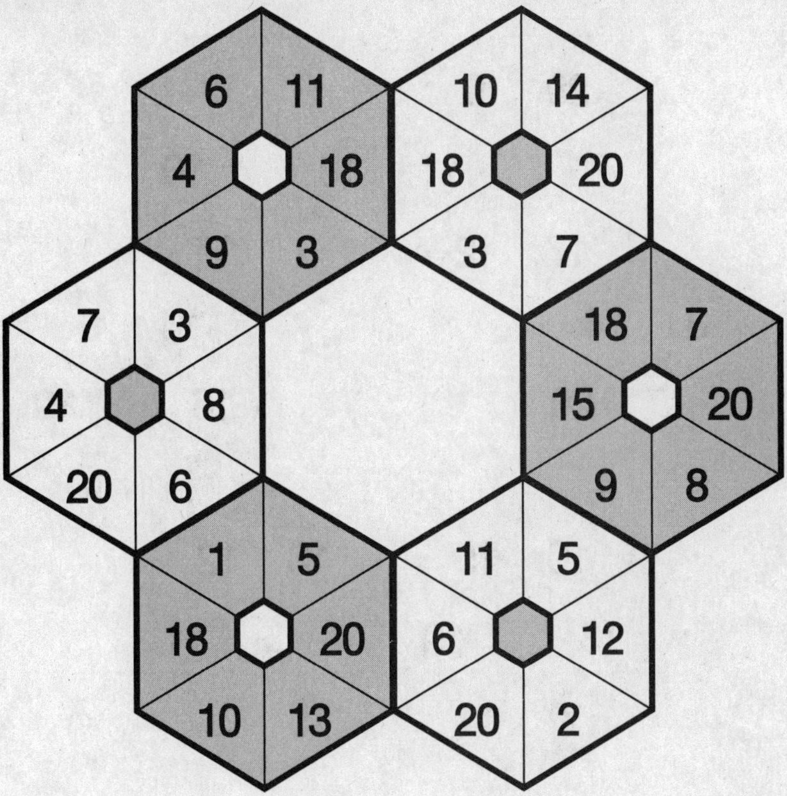

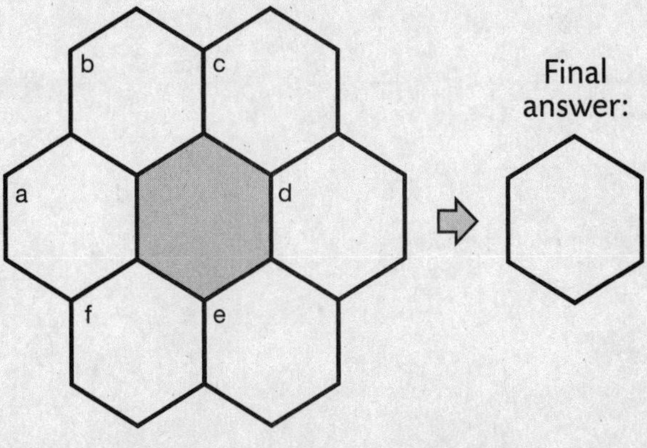

KAKOOMA EASY 6 ADDITION

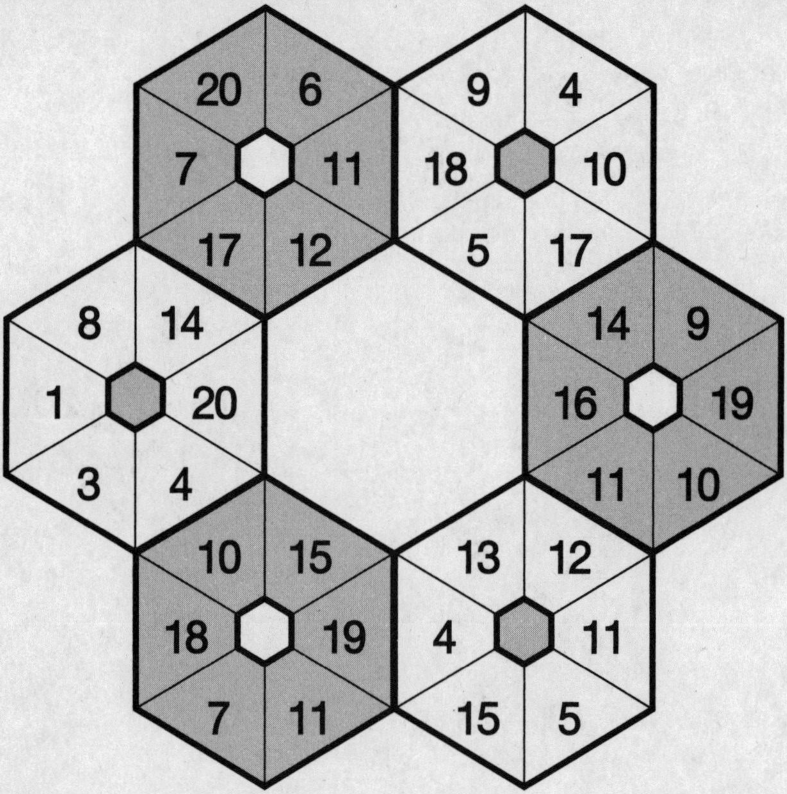

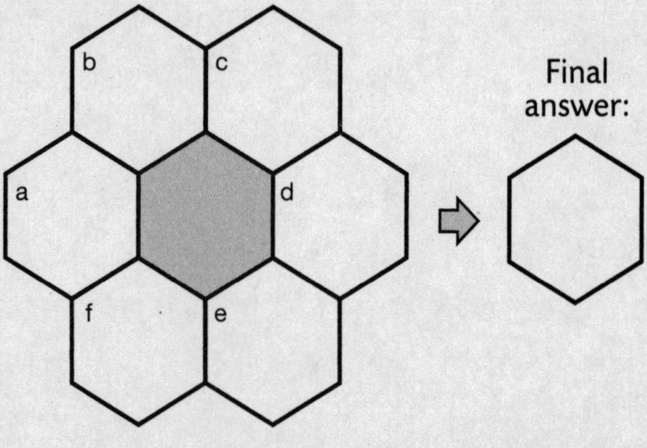

KAKOOMA EASY 6 ADDITION

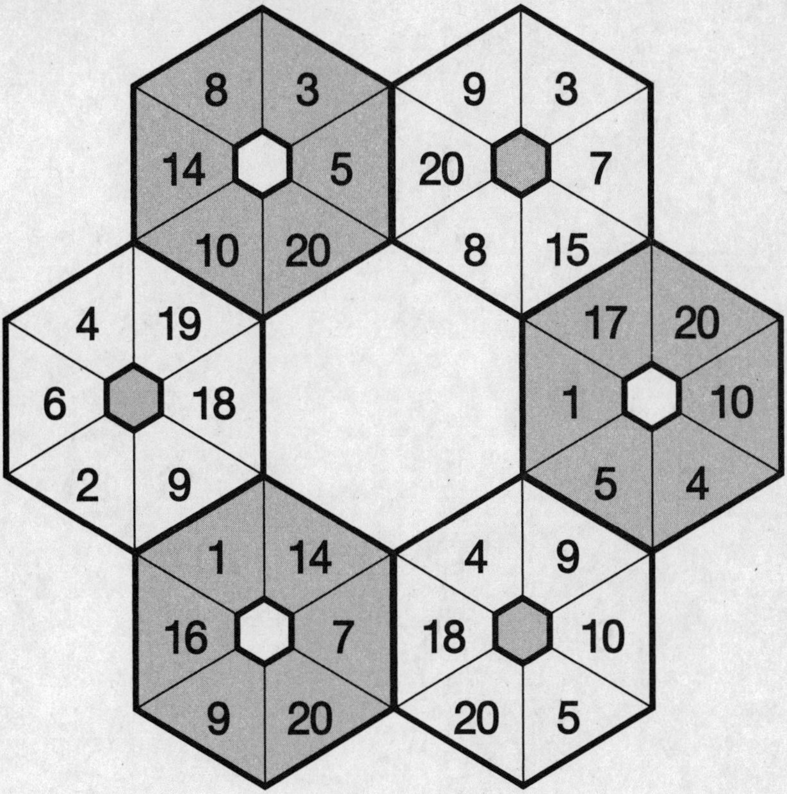

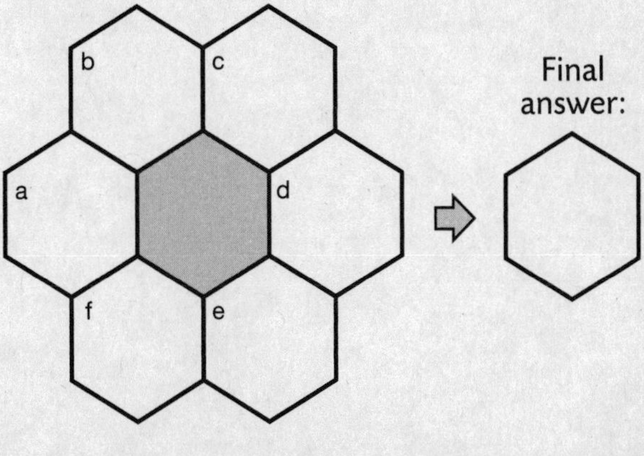

KAKOOMA EASY 6 ADDITION

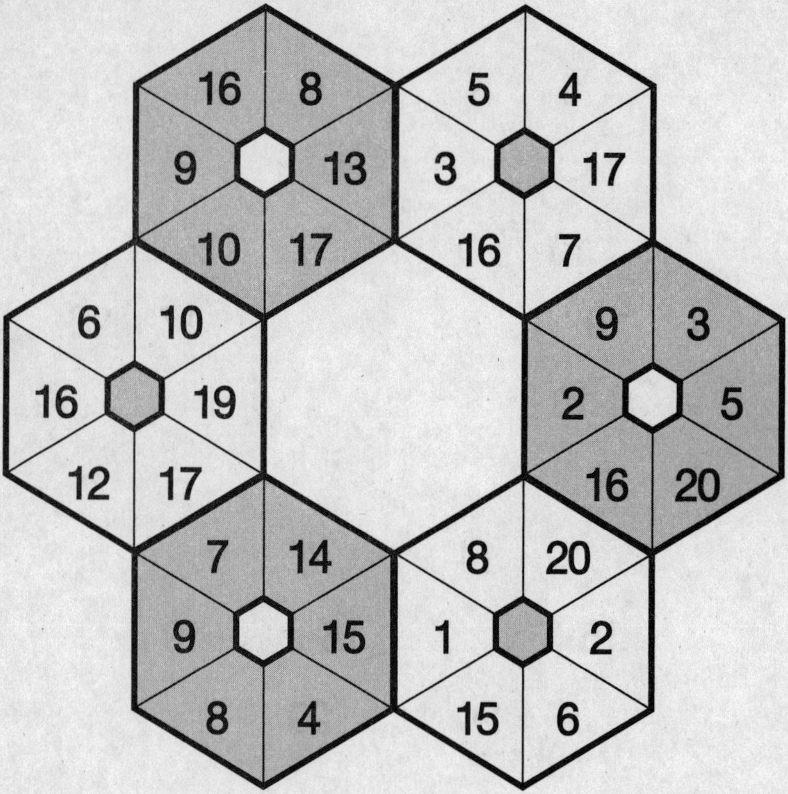

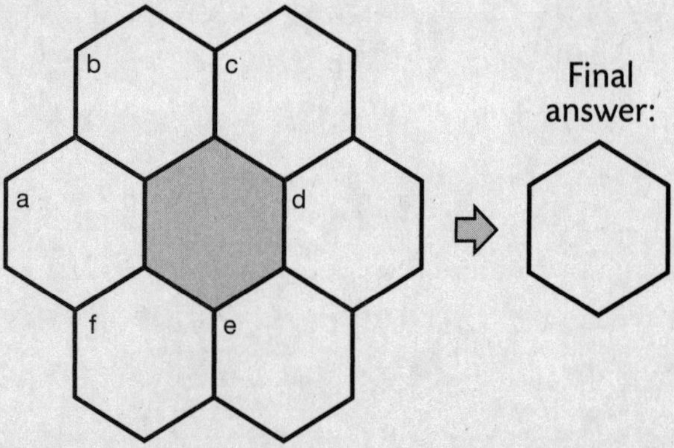

KAKOOMA EASY 6 ADDITION

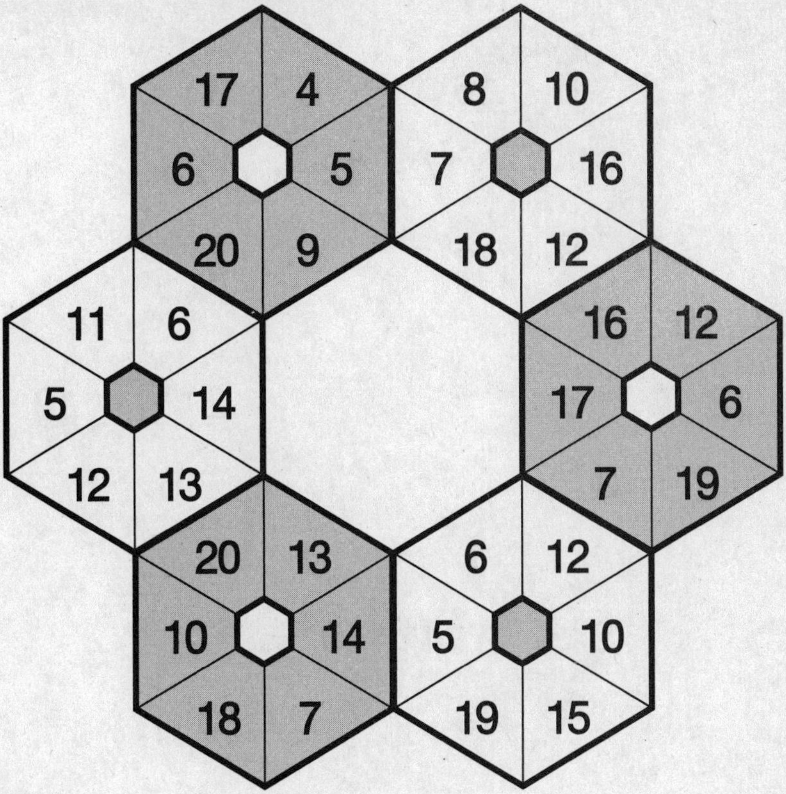

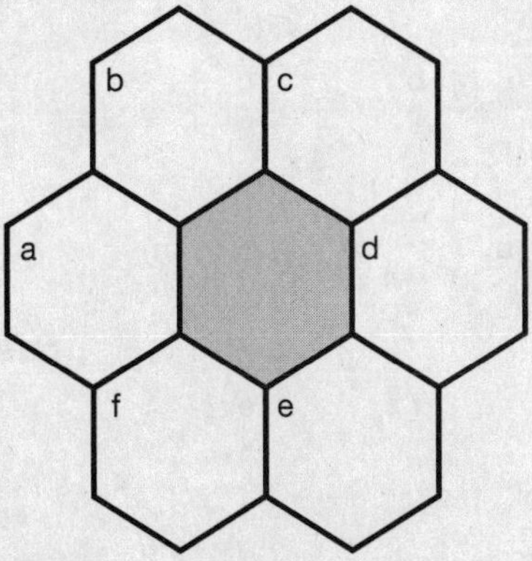

Final answer:

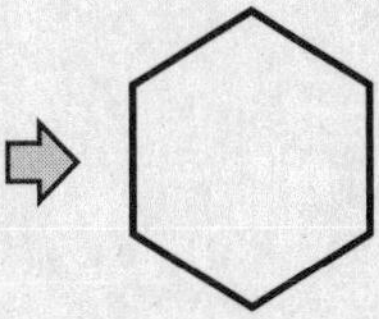

KAKOOMA EASY 6 ADDITION

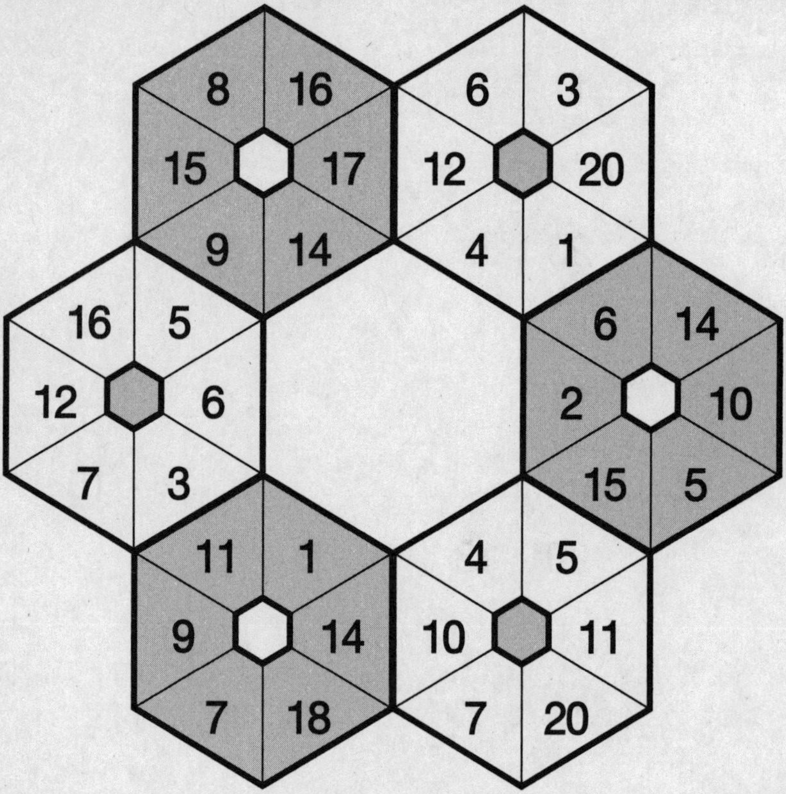

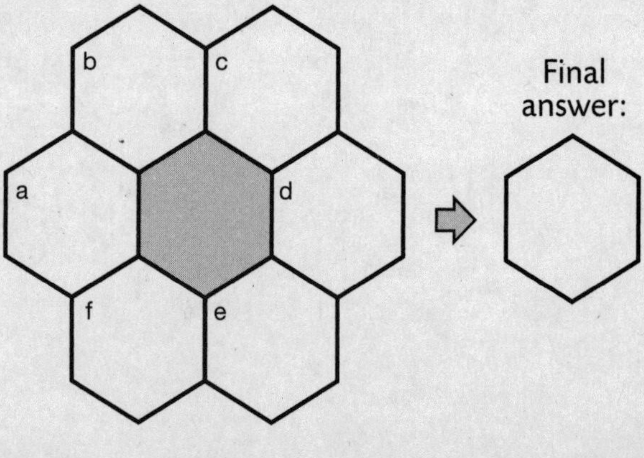

KAKOOMA EASY 6 ADDITION

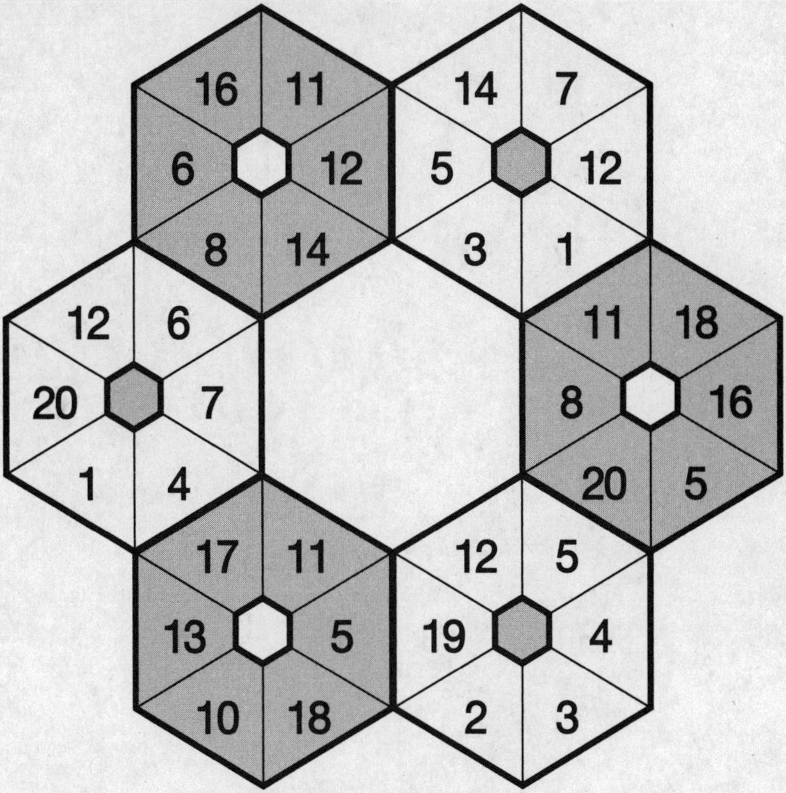

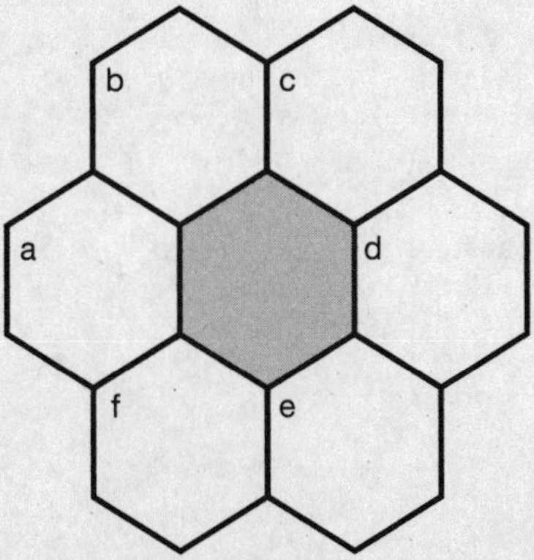

Final answer:

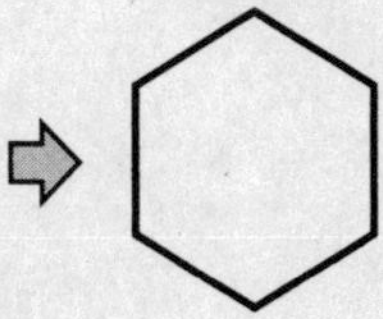

KAKOOMA EASY 6 ADDITION

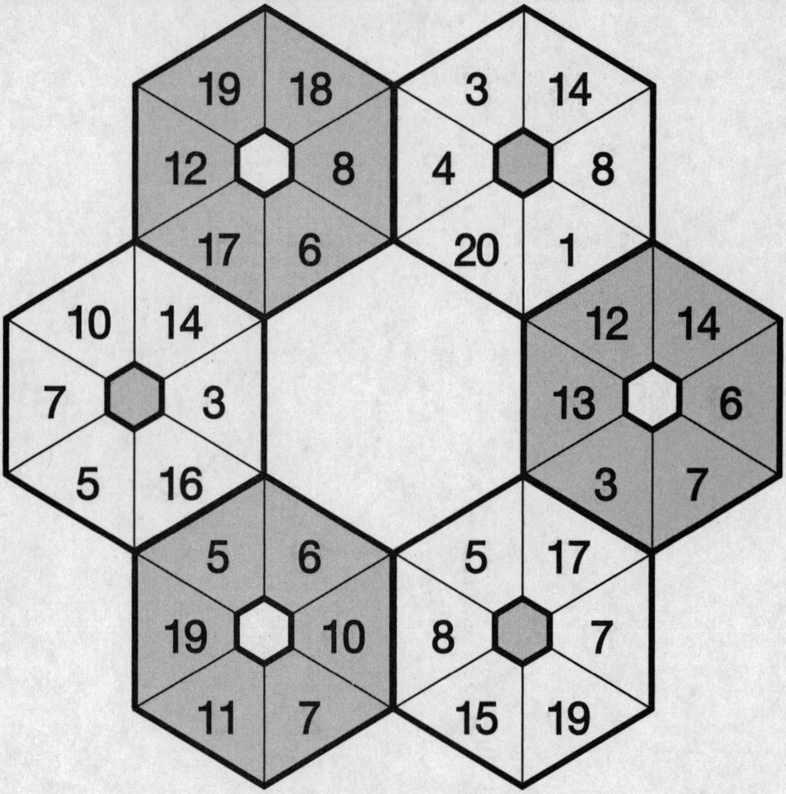

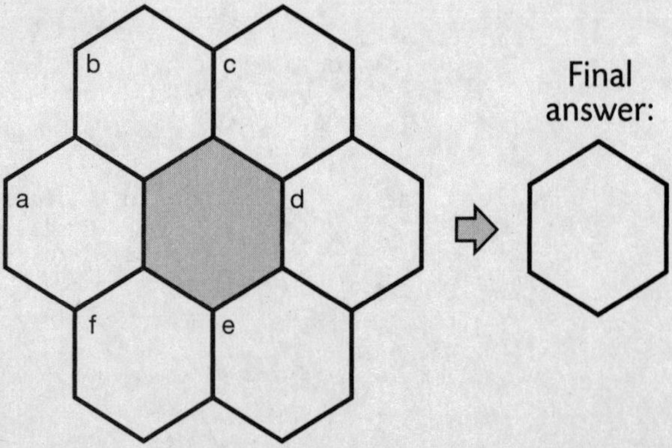

KAKOOMA EASY 6 ADDITION

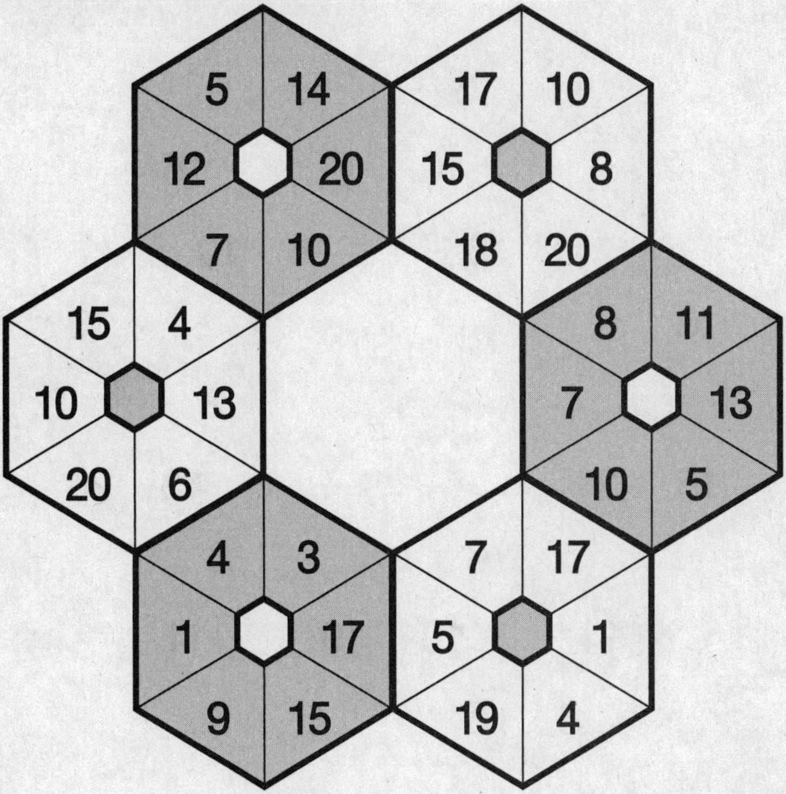

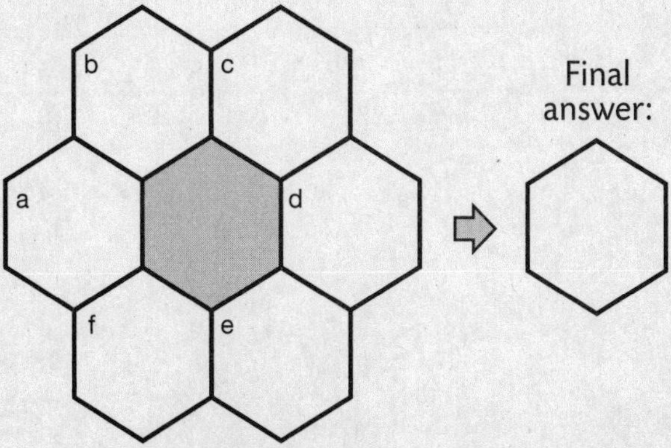

KAKOOMA EASY 6 ADDITION

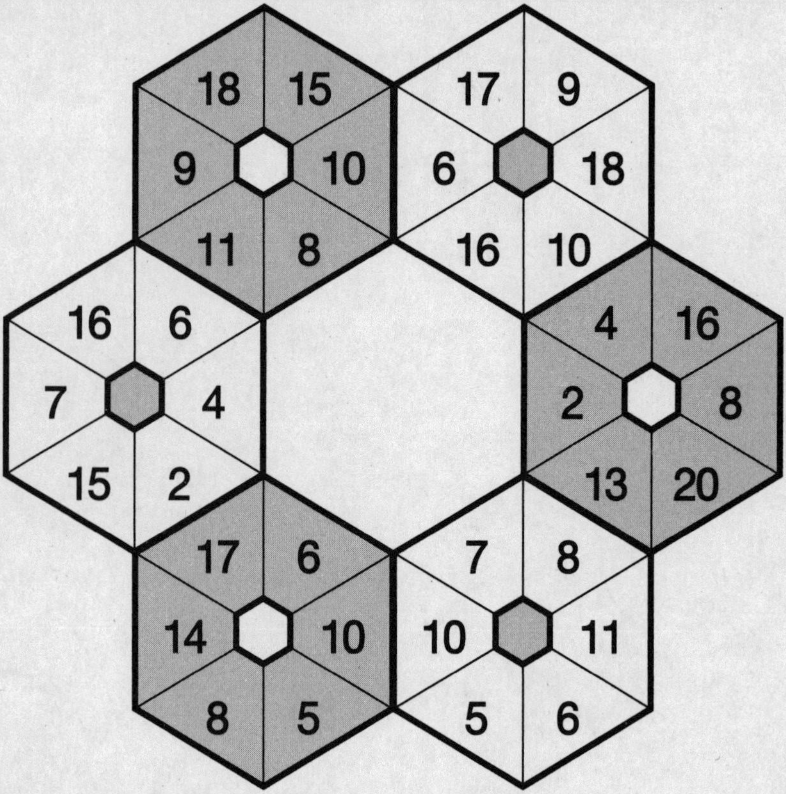

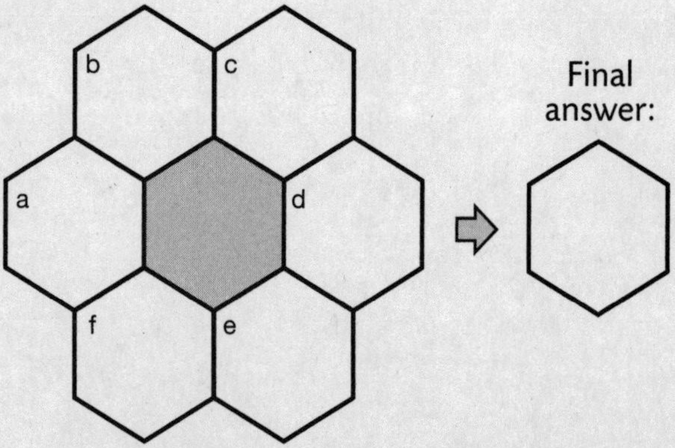

KAKOOMA EASY 6 ADDITION

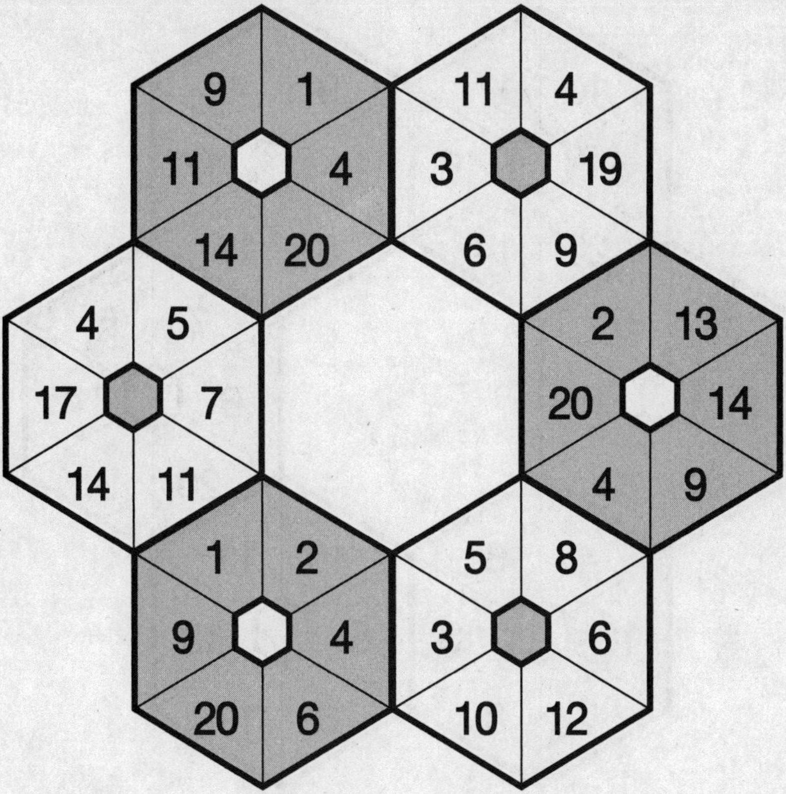

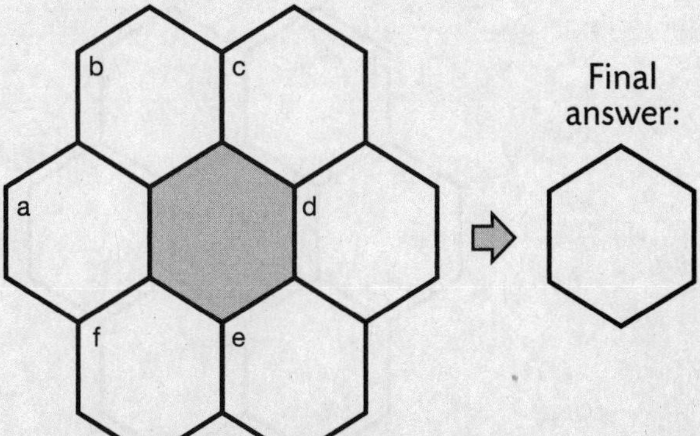

KAKOOMA EASY 6 ADDITION

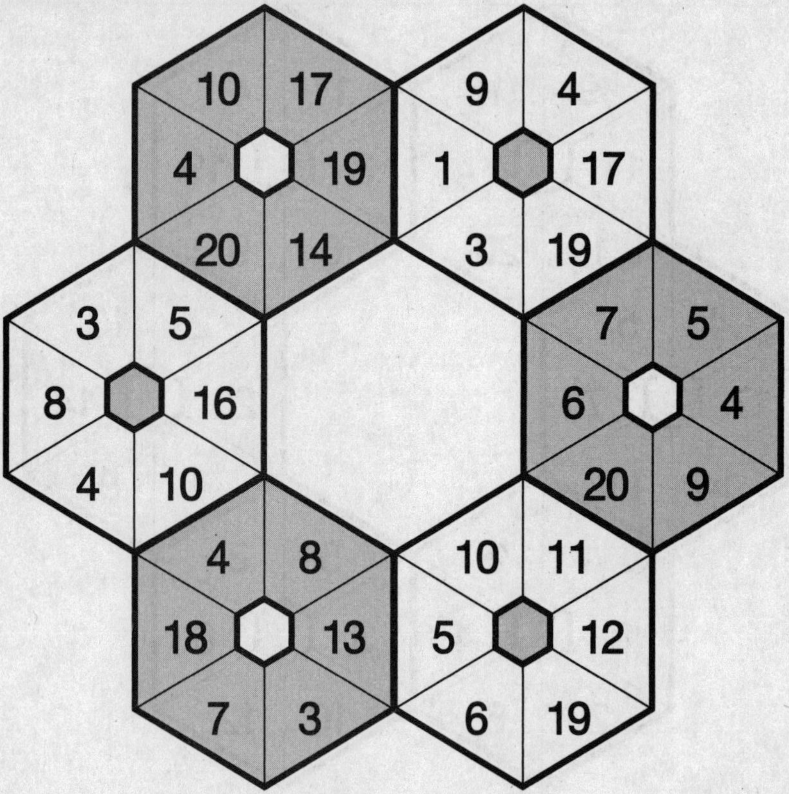

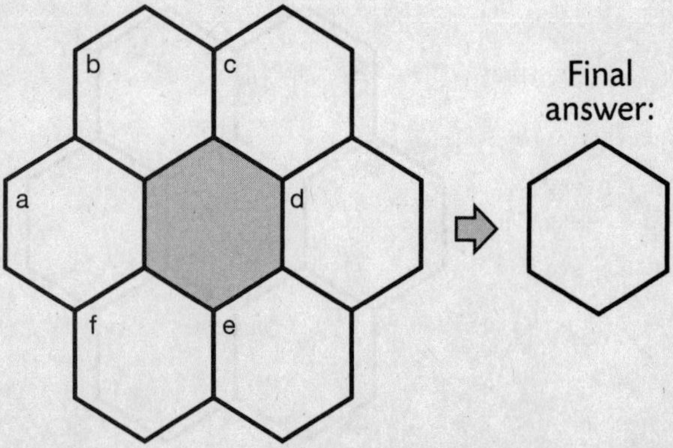

KAKOOMA EASY 6 ADDITION

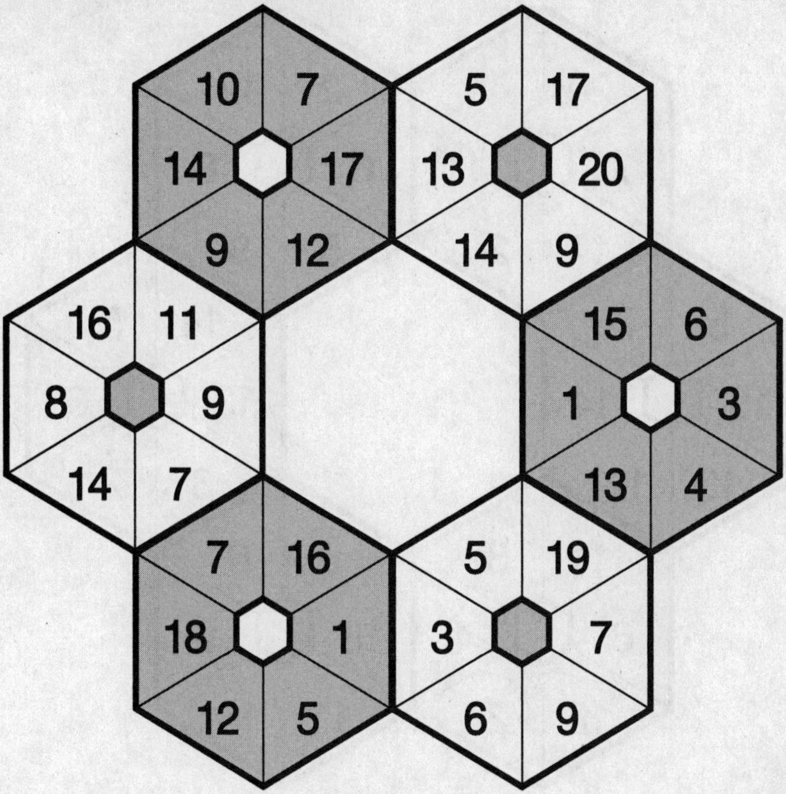

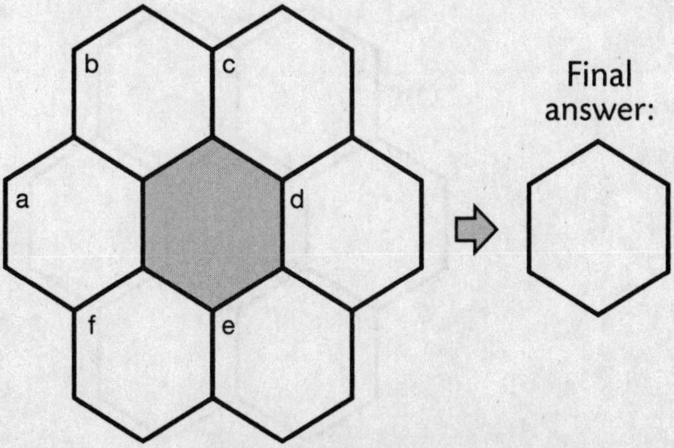

KAKOOMA EASY 6 ADDITION

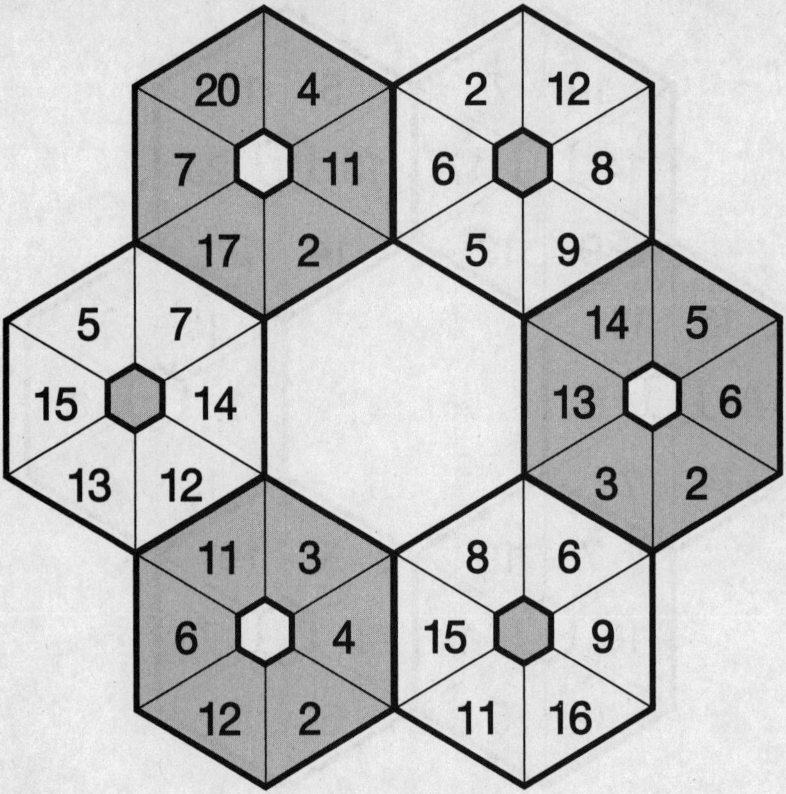

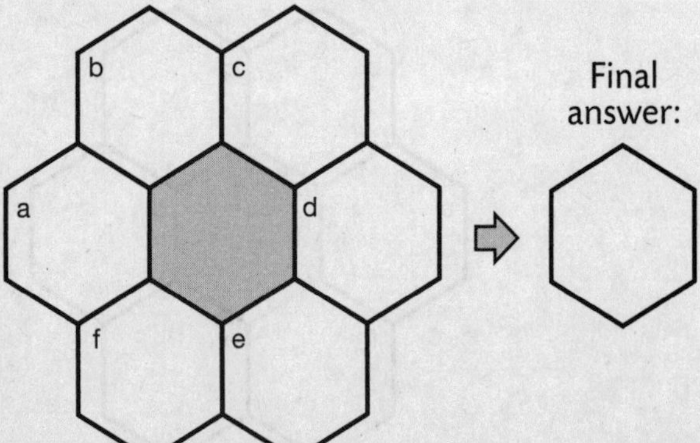

KAKOOMA EASY 6 ADDITION

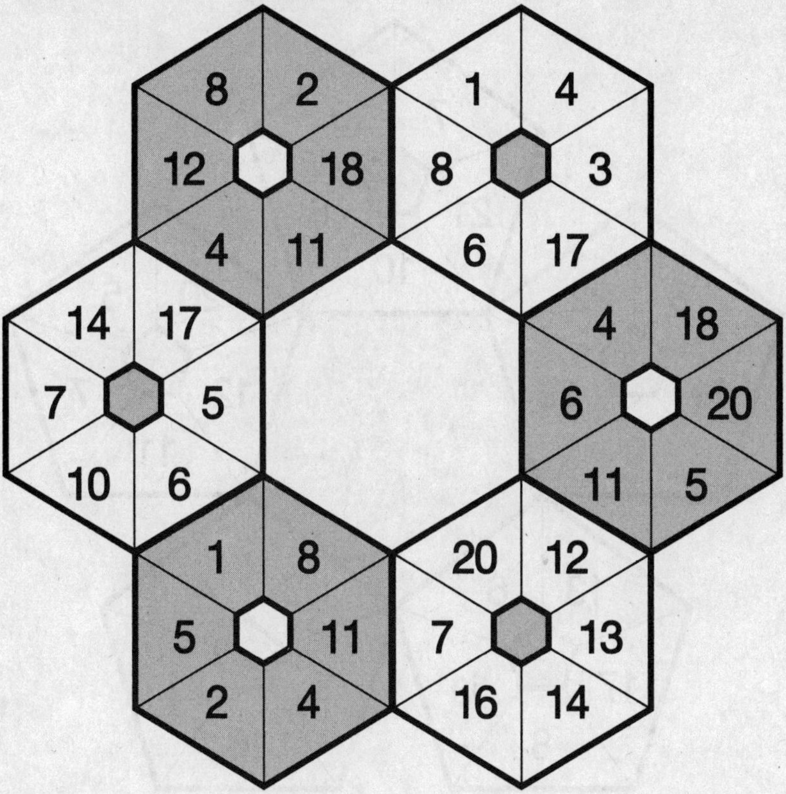

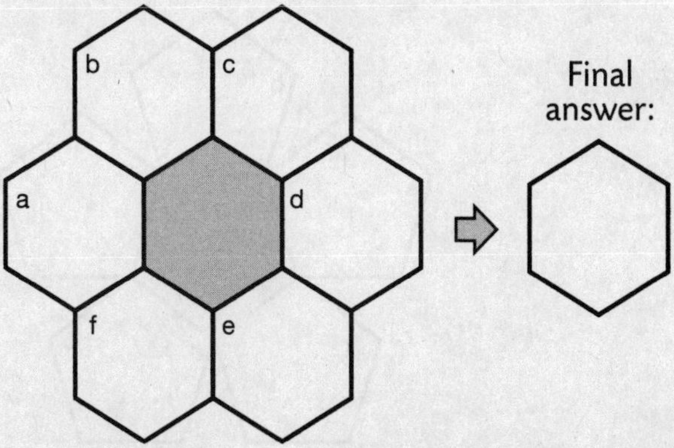

KAKOOMA HARD 5 ADDITION

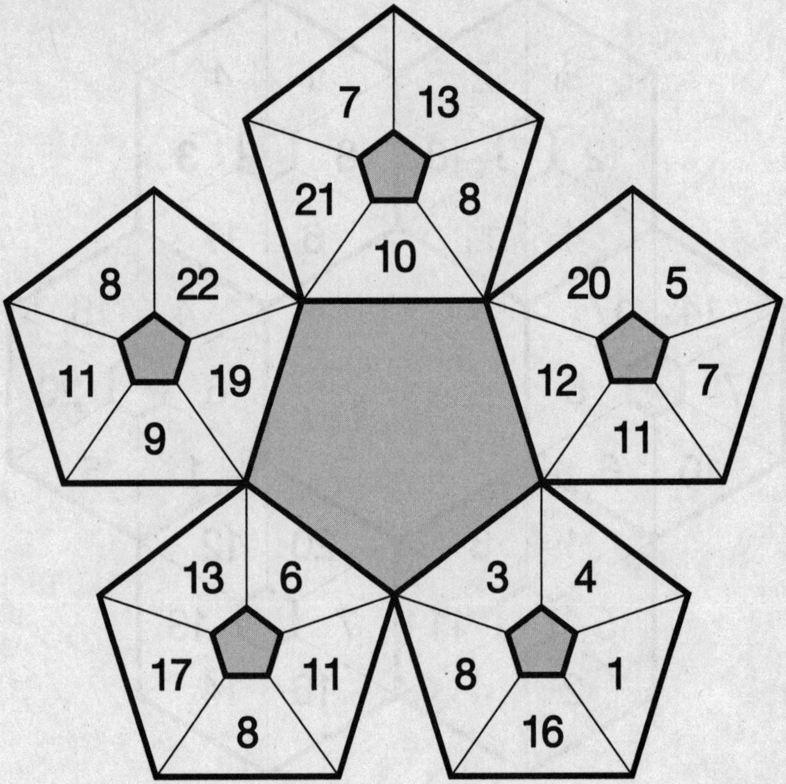

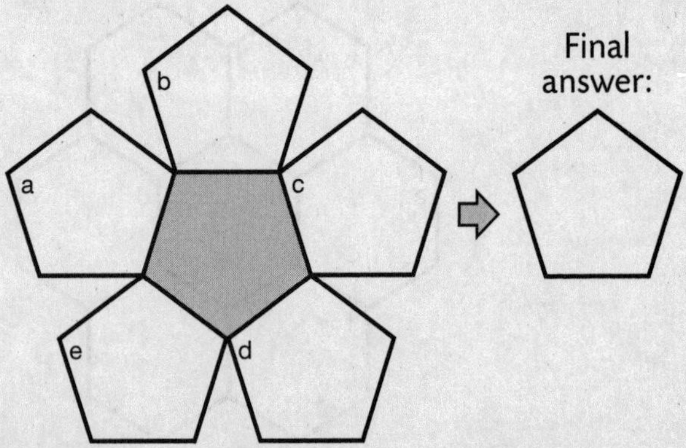

KAKOOMA HARD 5 ADDITION

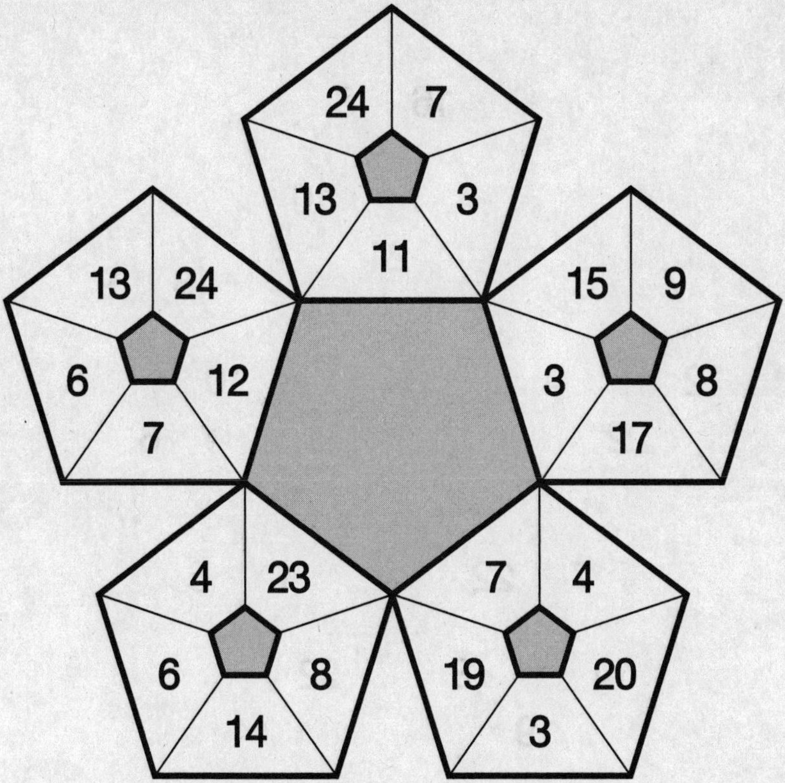

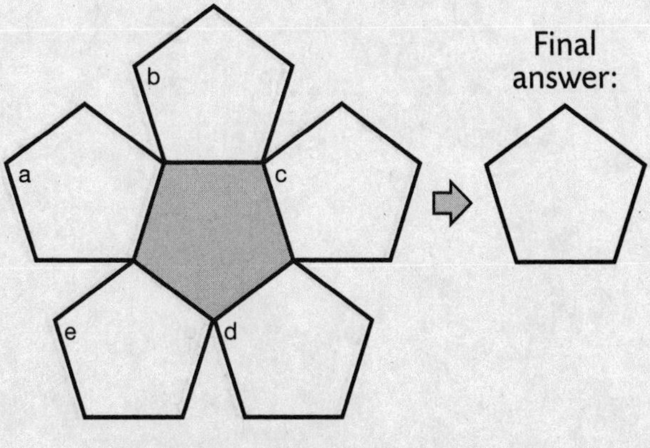

KAKOOMA HARD 5 ADDITION

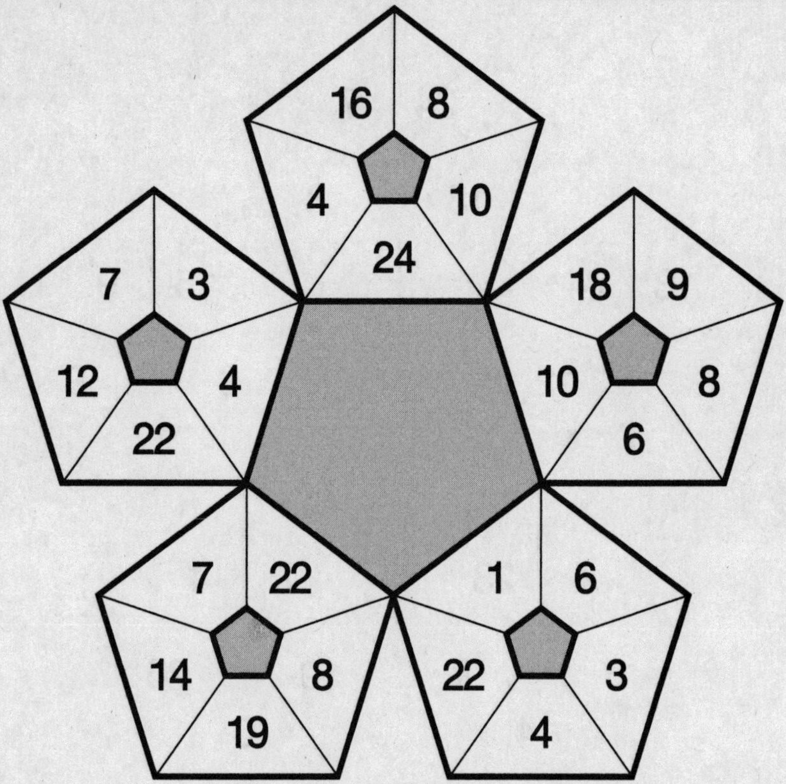

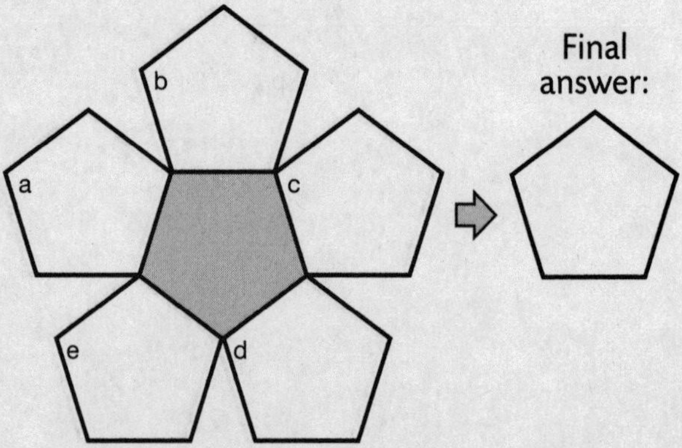

KAKOOMA HARD 5 ADDITION

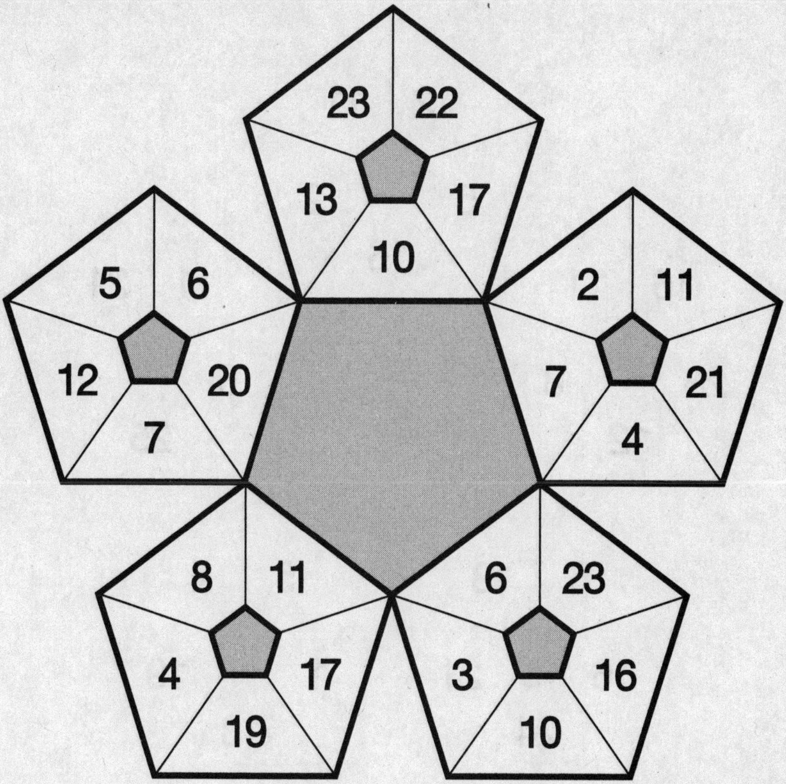

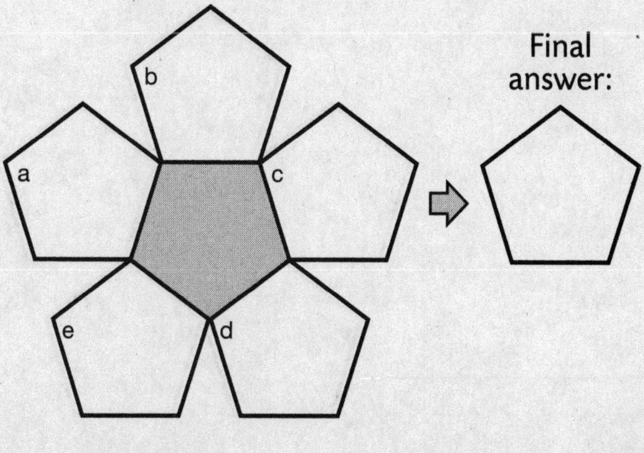

KAKOOMA HARD 5 ADDITION

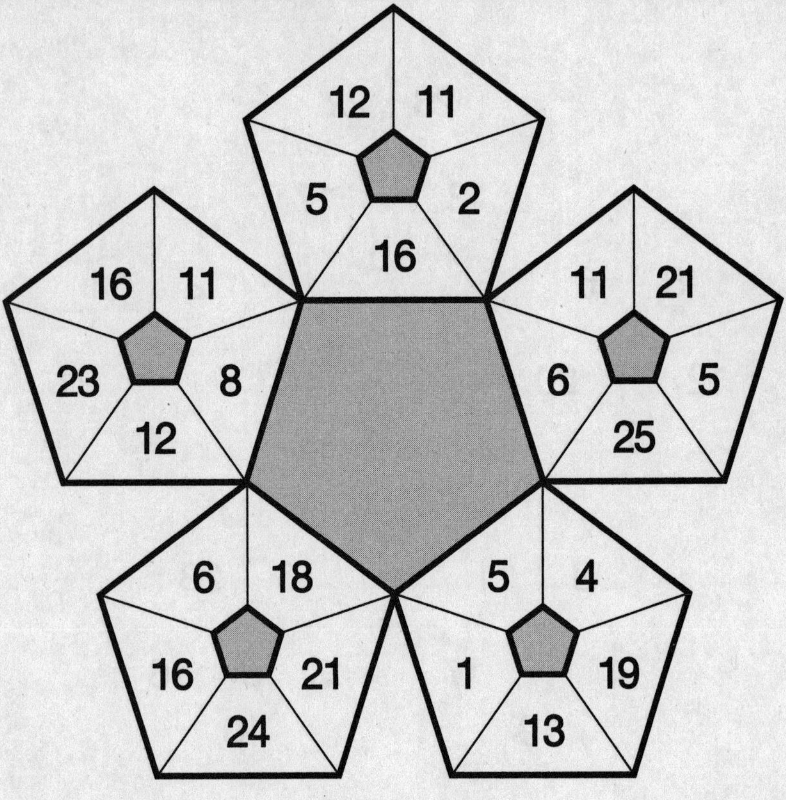

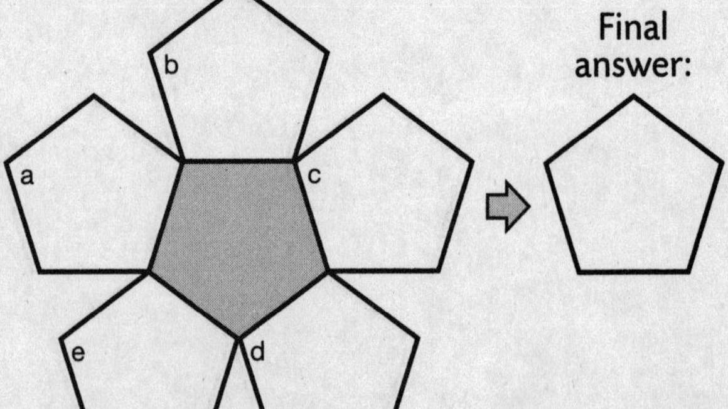

KAKOOMA HARD 5 ADDITION

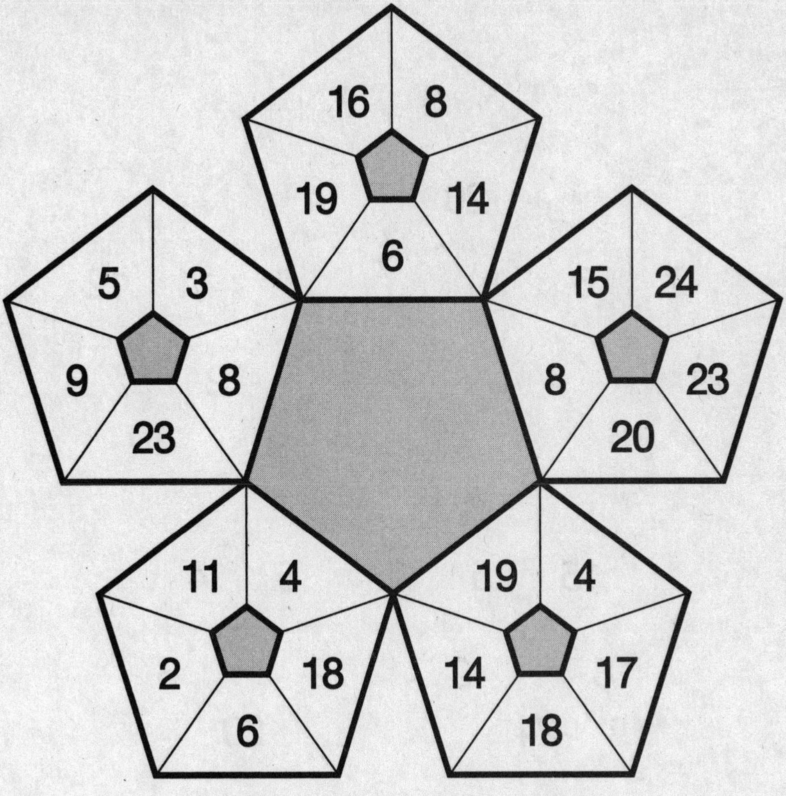

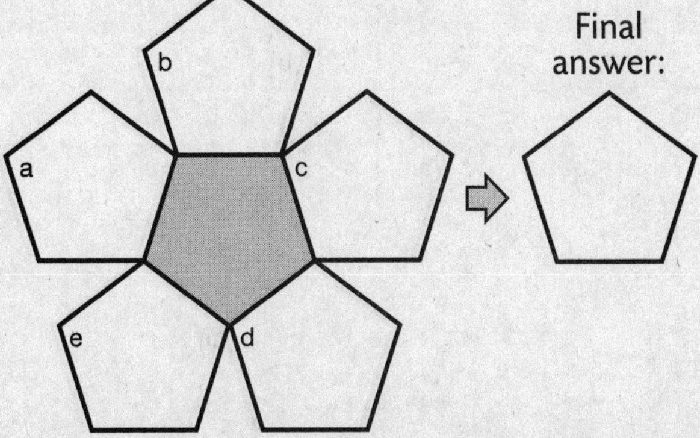

KAKOOMA HARD 5 ADDITION

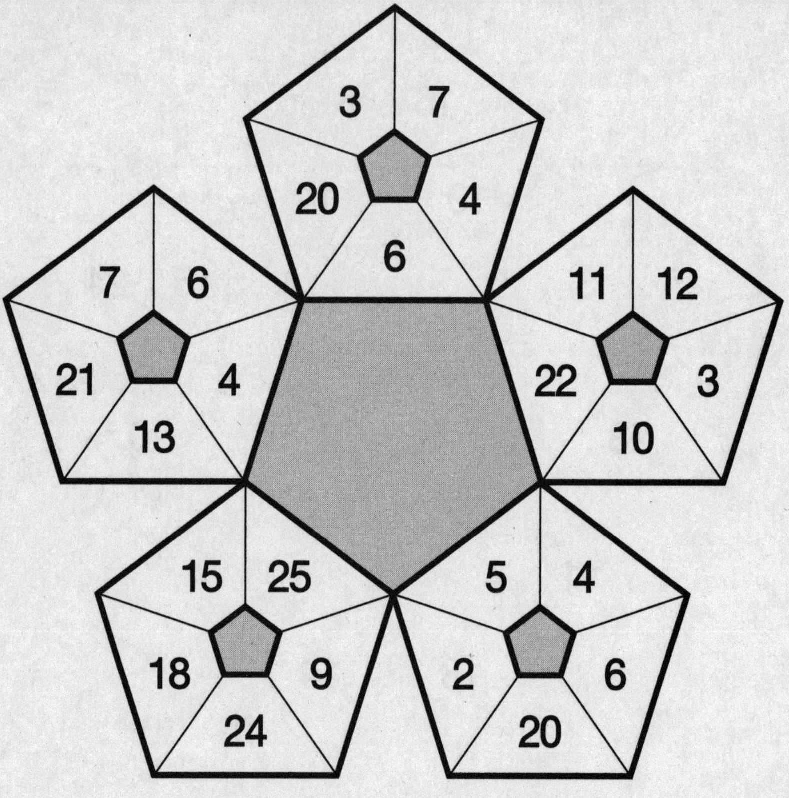

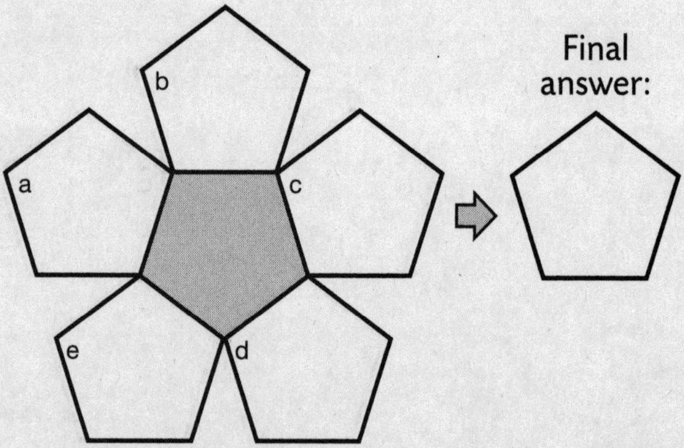

KAKOOMA HARD 5 ADDITION

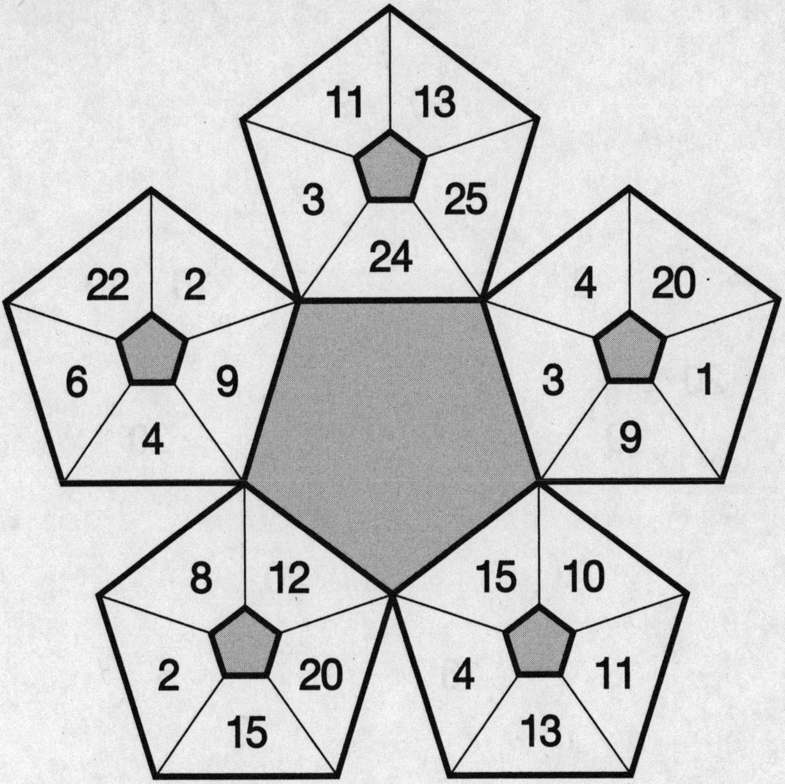

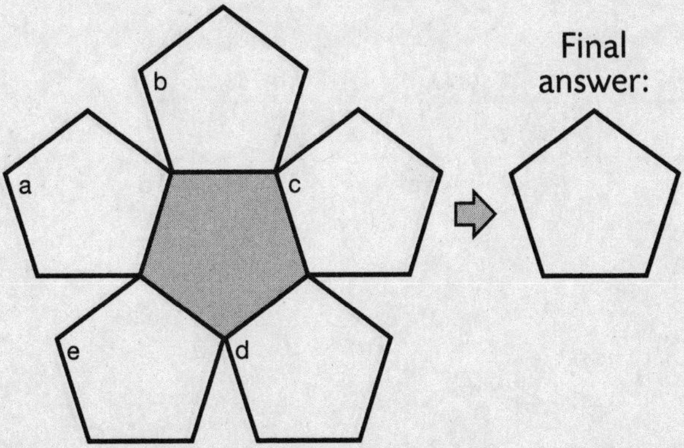

KAKOOMA HARD 5 ADDITION

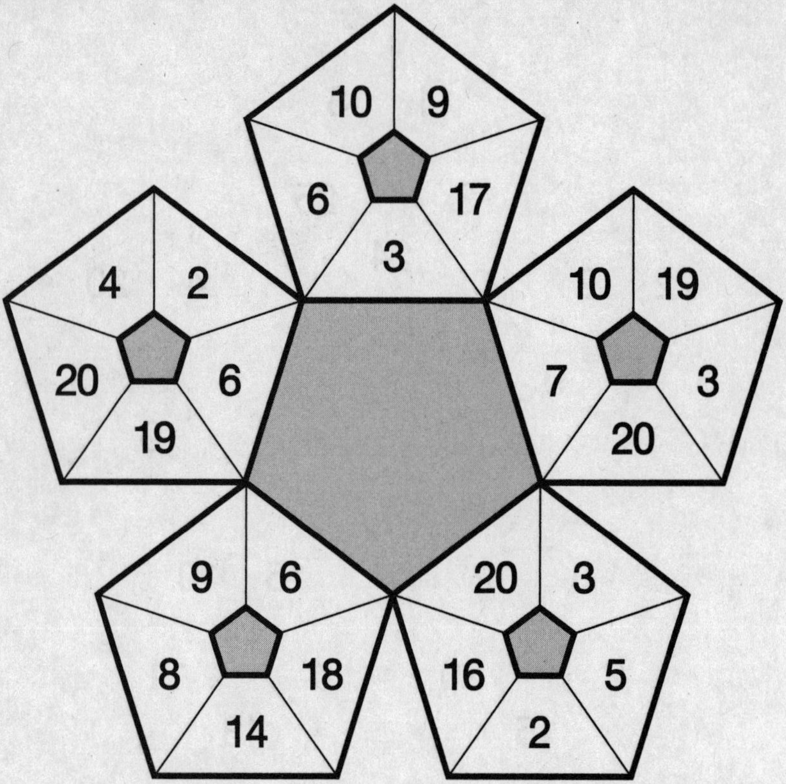

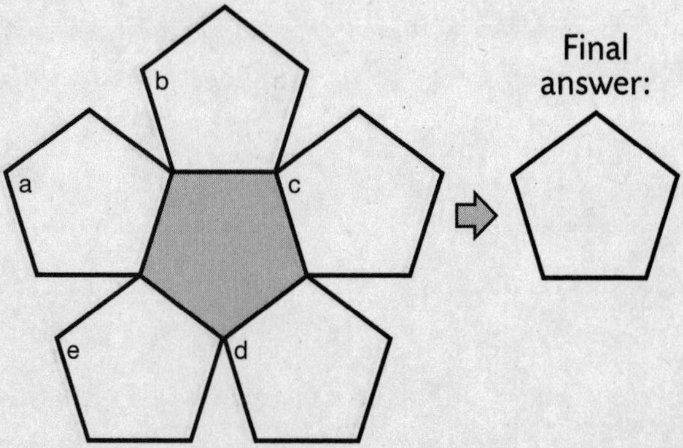

KAKOOMA HARD 5 ADDITION

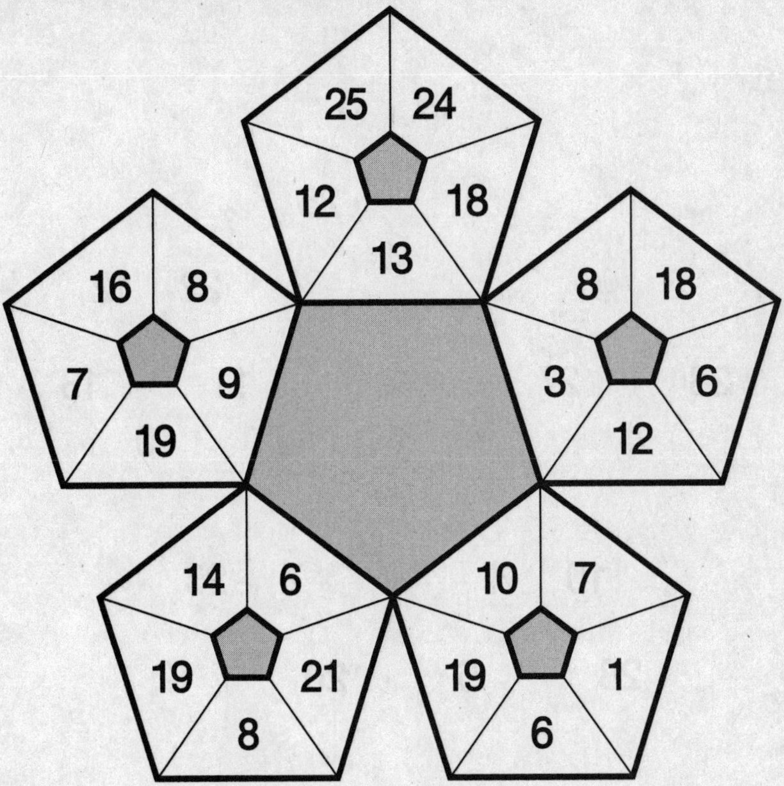

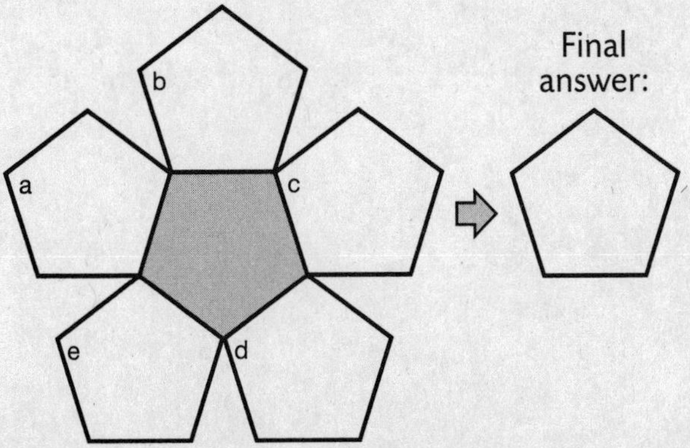

KAKOOMA HARD 5 ADDITION

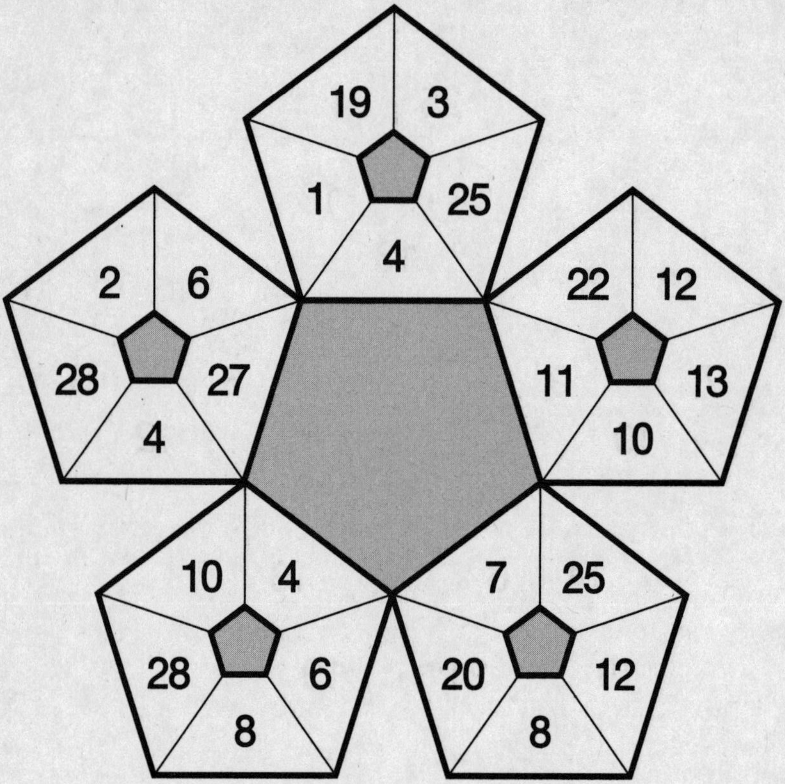

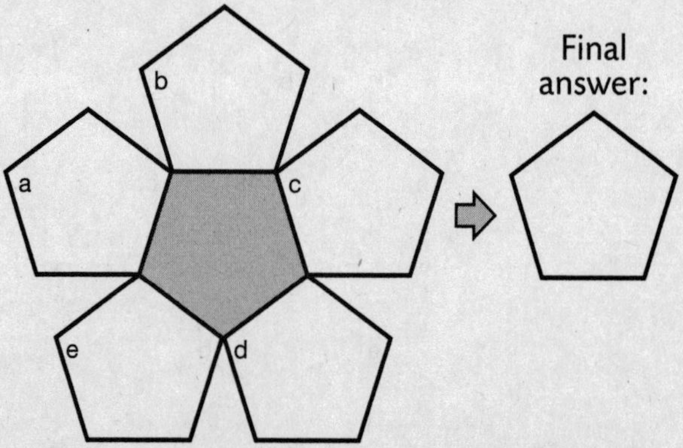

KAKOOMA HARD 5 ADDITION

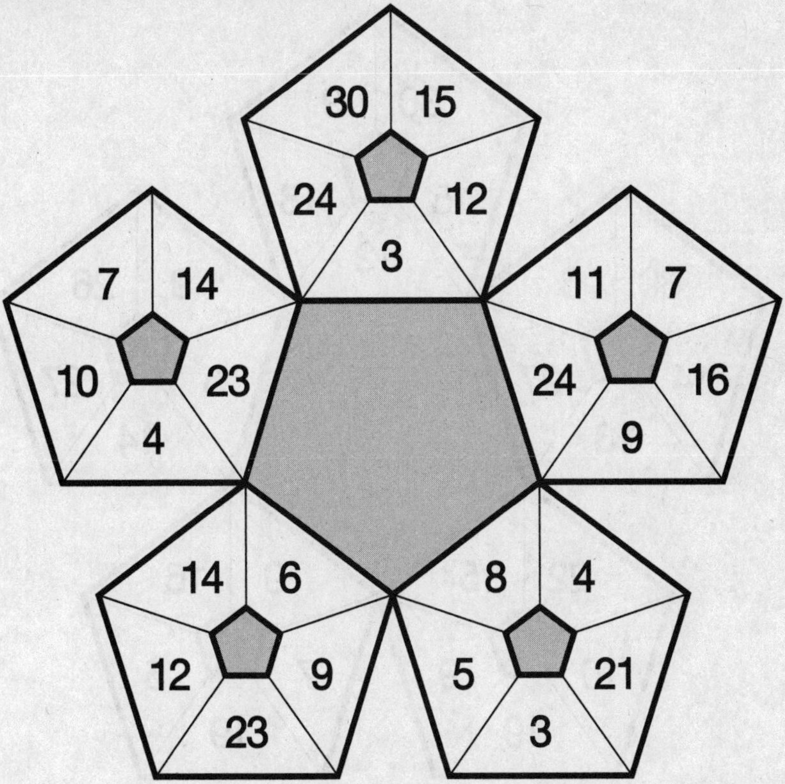

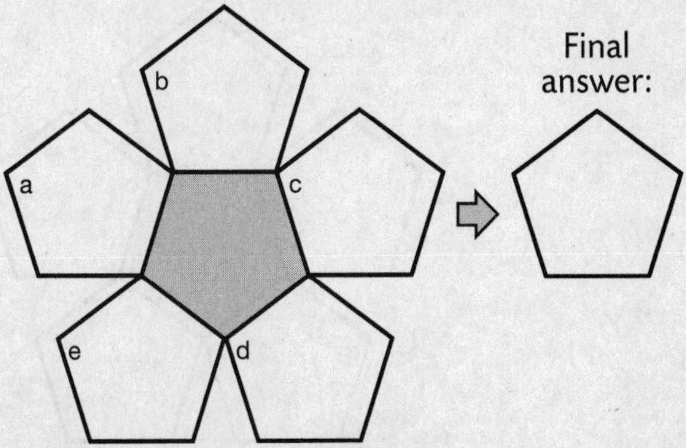

KAKOOMA HARD 5 ADDITION

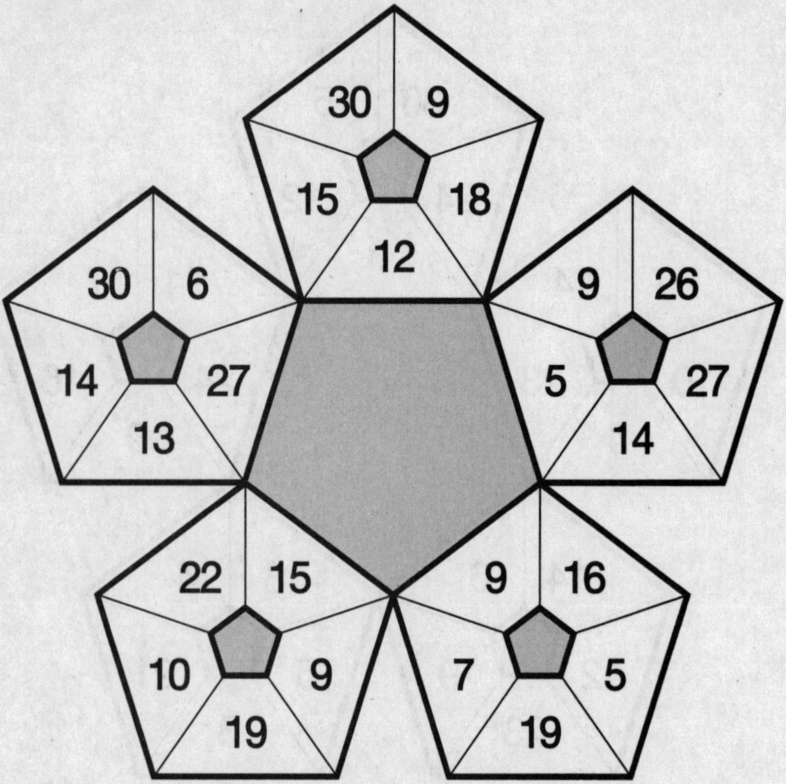

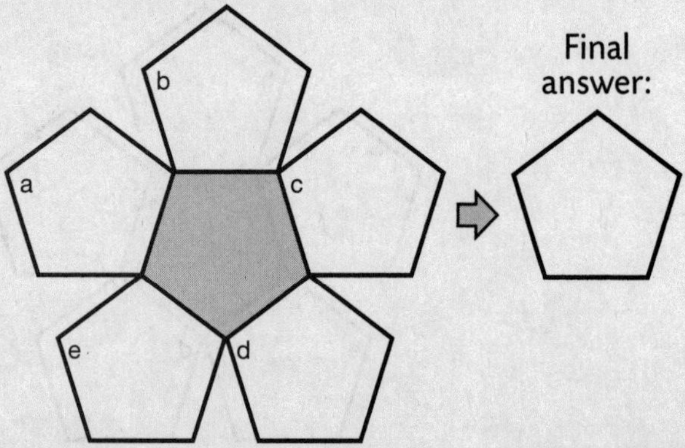

KAKOOMA HARD 5 ADDITION

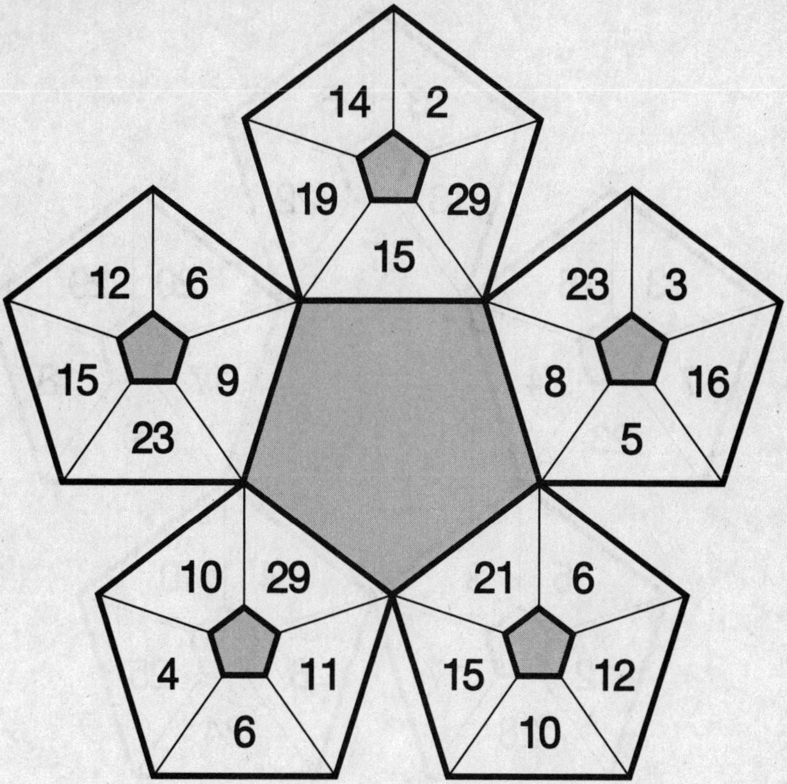

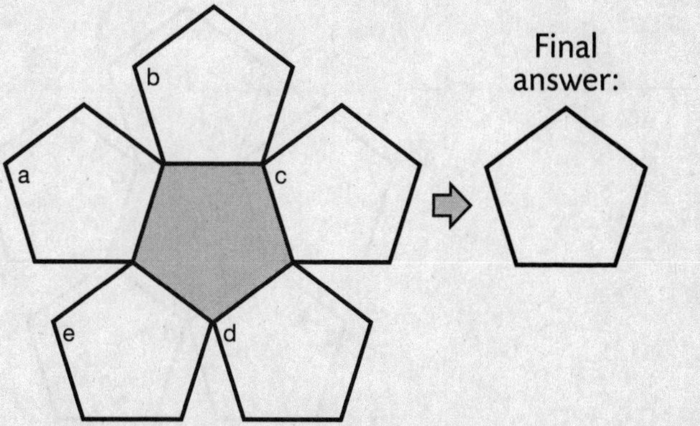

KAKOOMA HARD 5 ADDITION

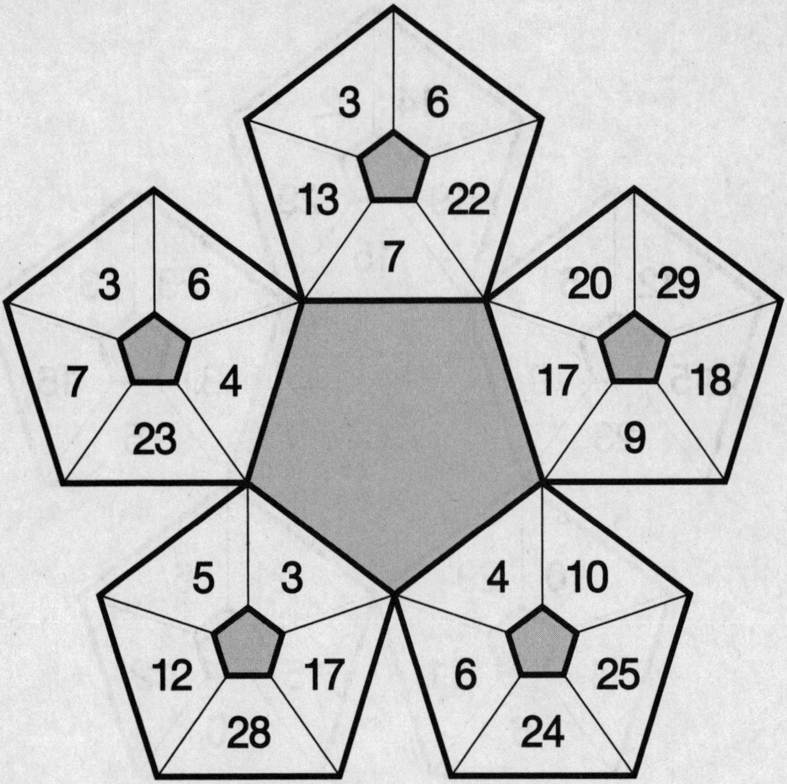

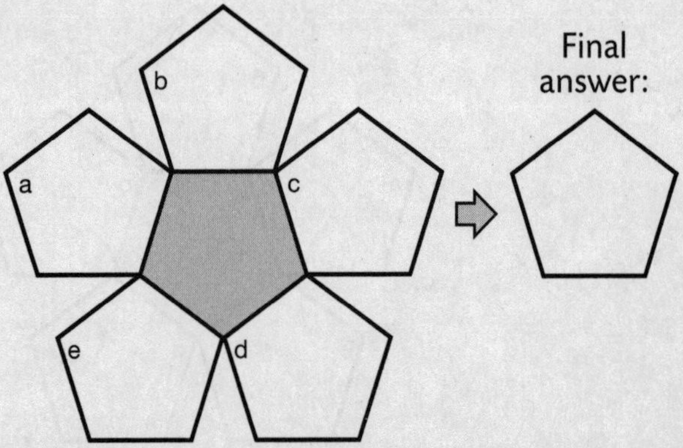

KAKOOMA HARD 5 ADDITION

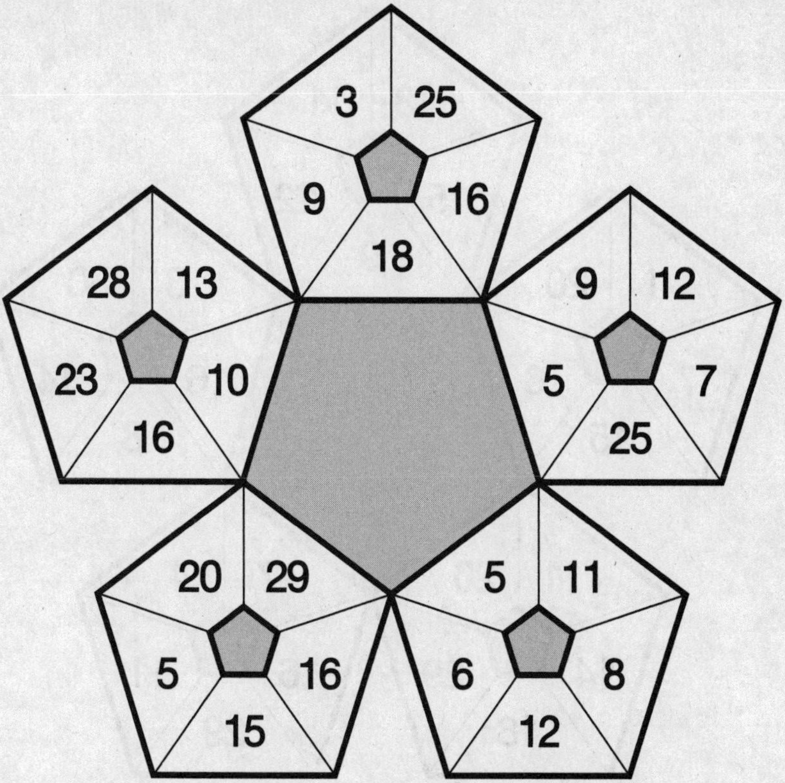

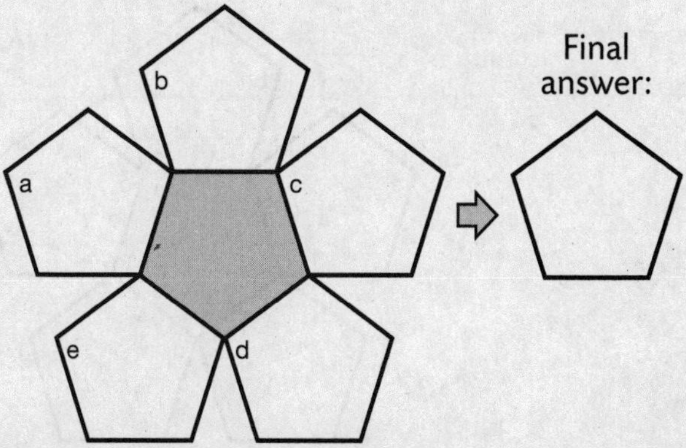

KAKOOMA HARD 5 ADDITION

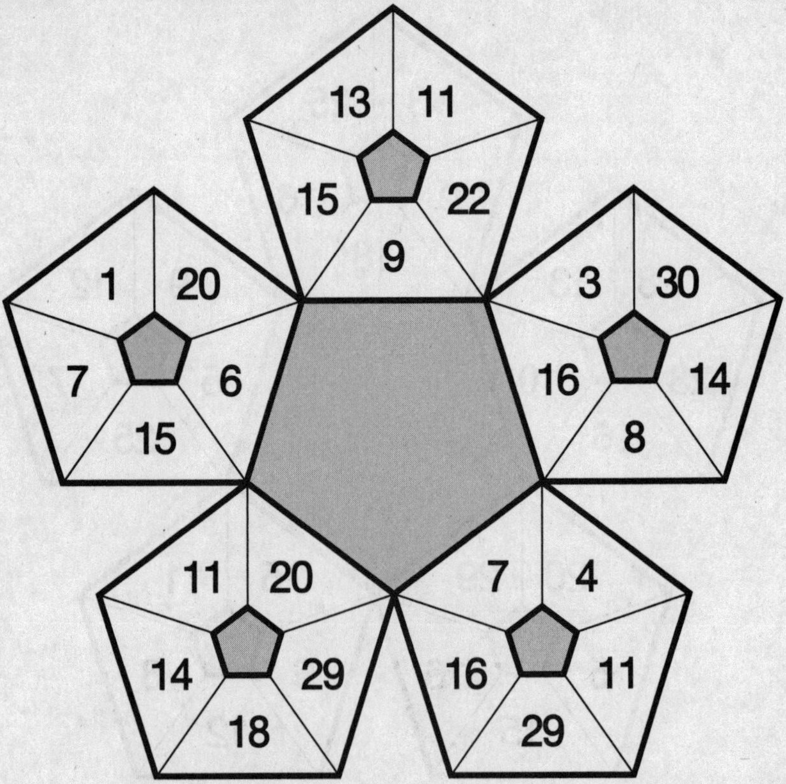

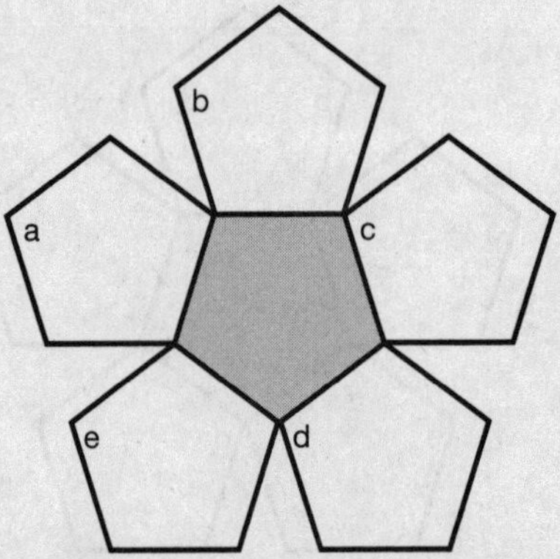

Final answer:

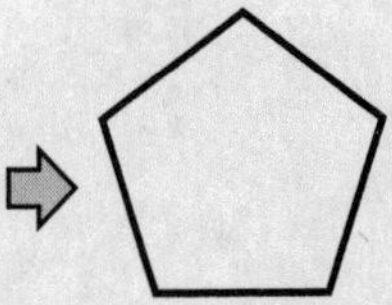

KAKOOMA HARD 5 ADDITION

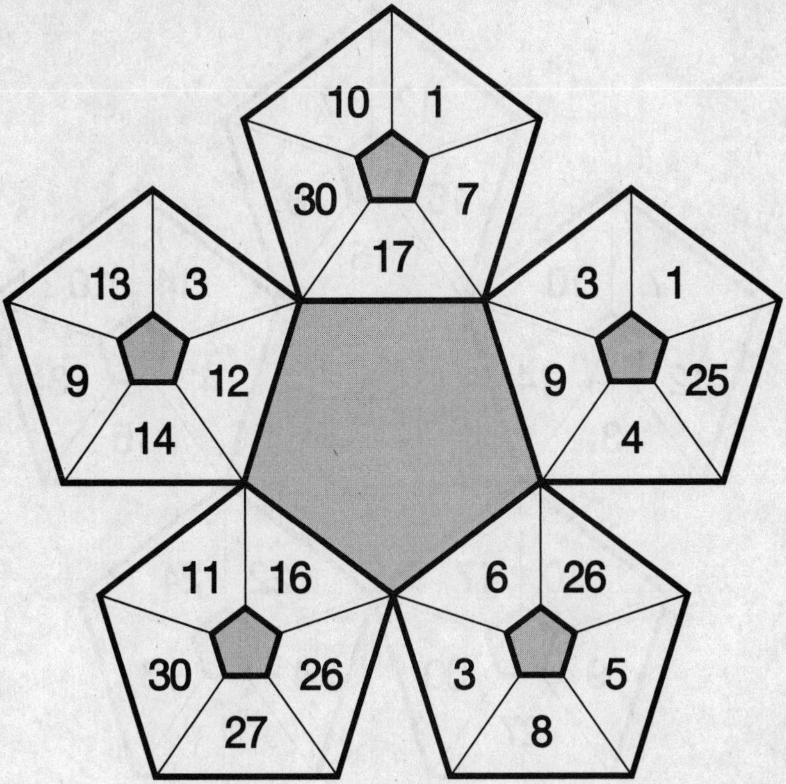

Final answer:

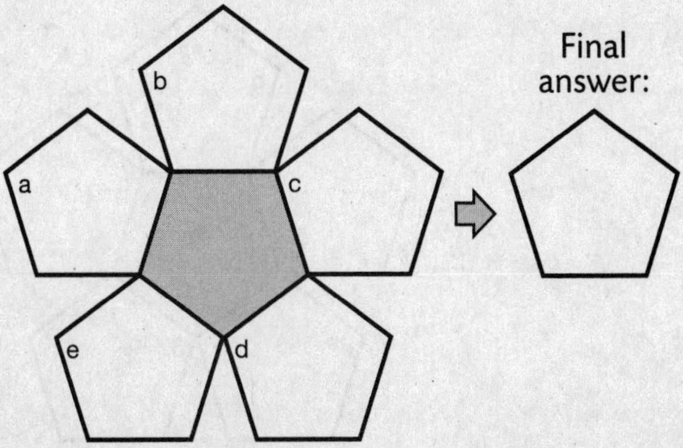

KAKOOMA HARD 5 ADDITION

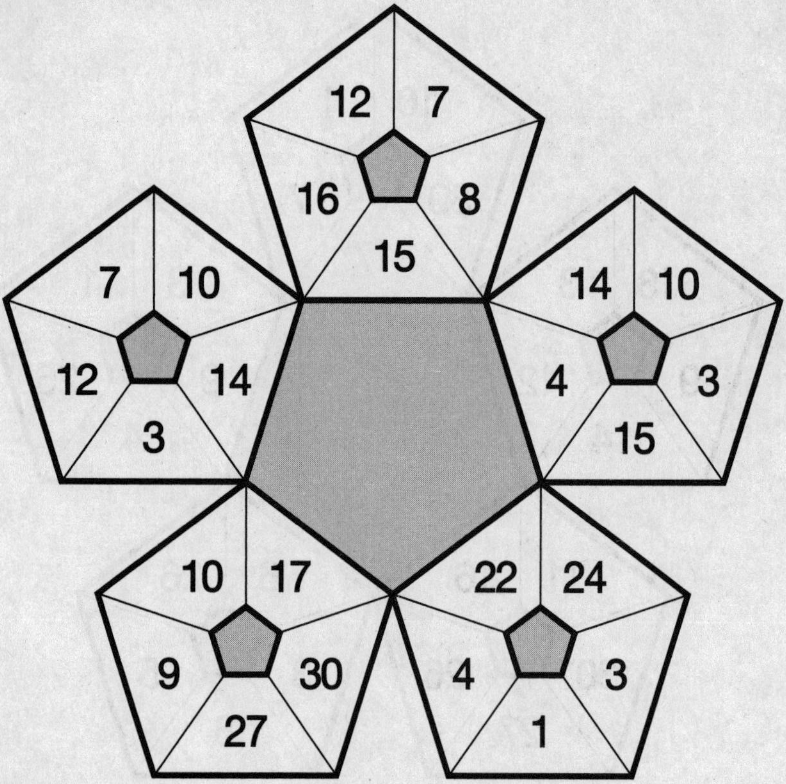

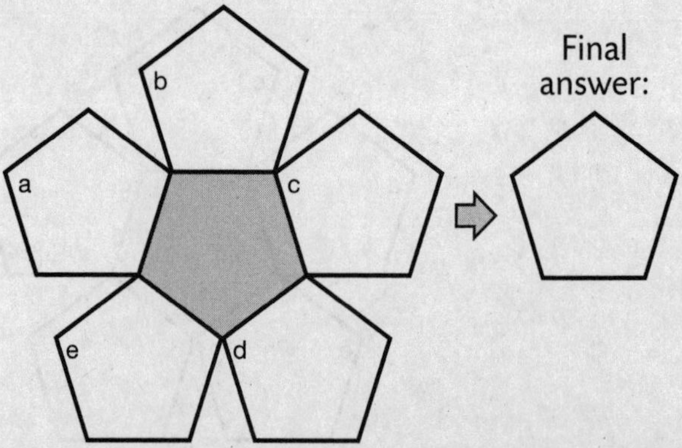

KAKOOMA HARD 5 ADDITION

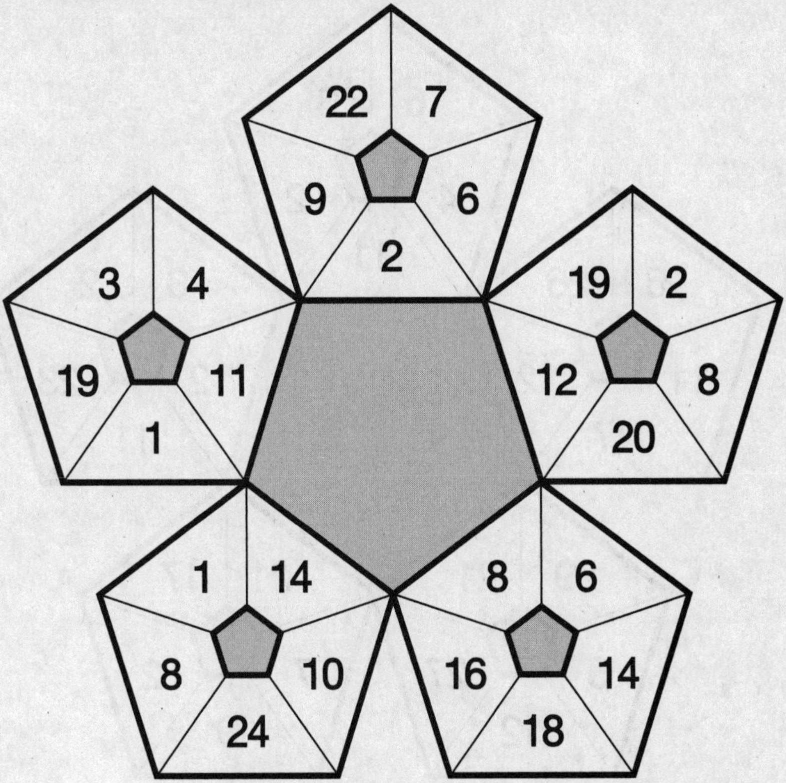

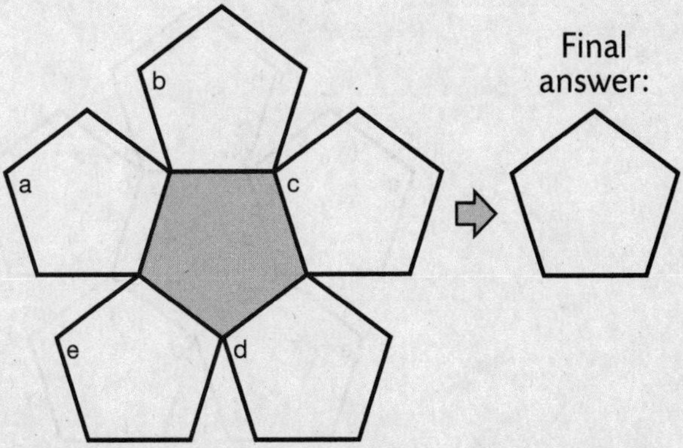

KAKOOMA HARD 5 ADDITION

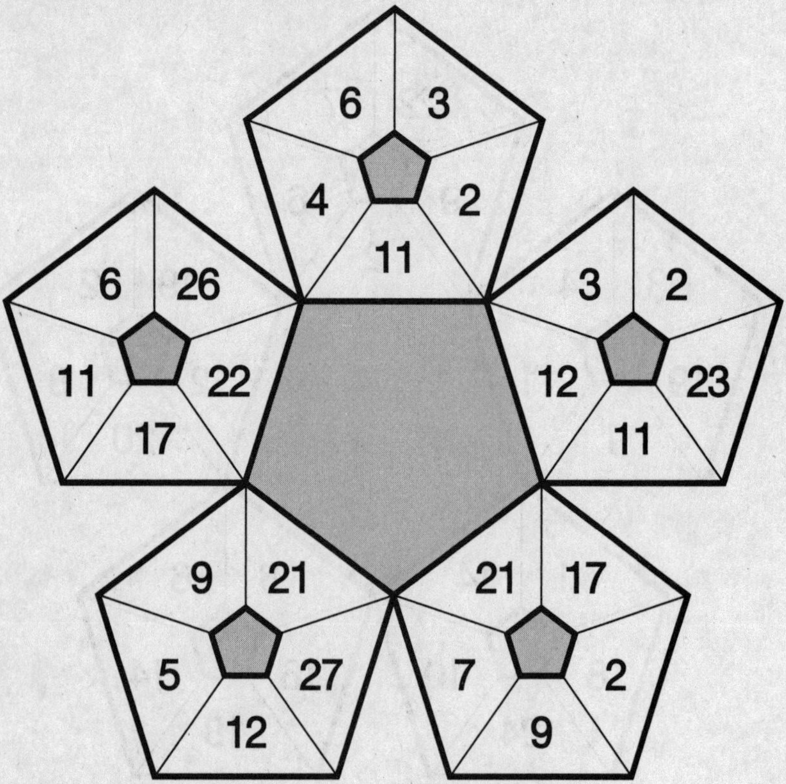

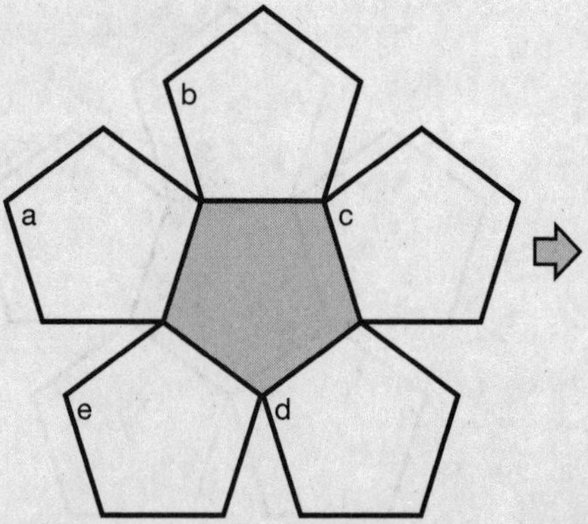

Final answer:

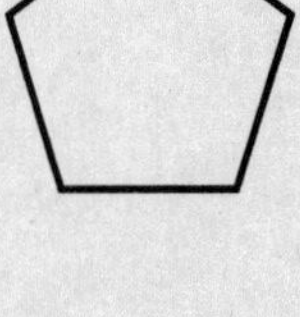

KAKOOMA HARD 6 ADDITION

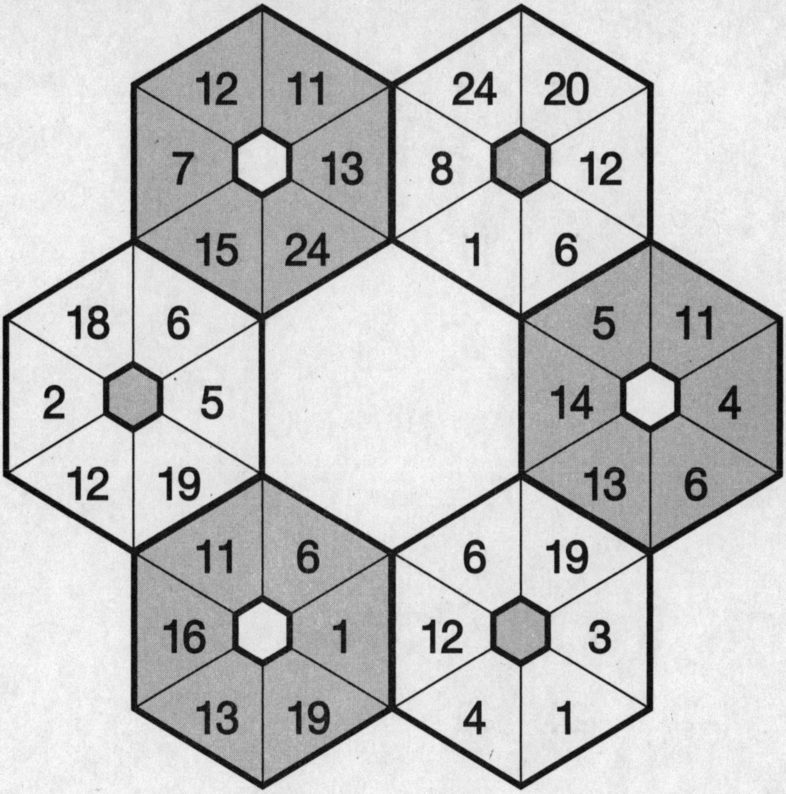

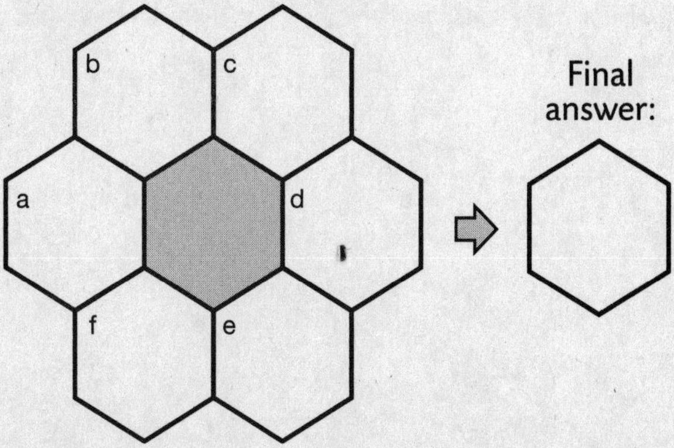

KAKOOMA HARD 6 ADDITION

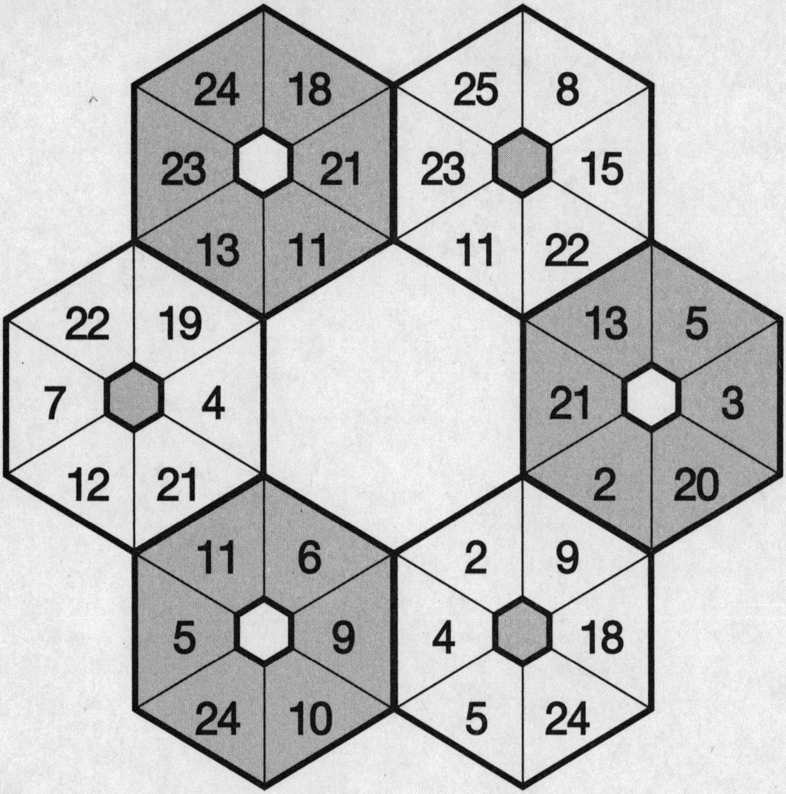

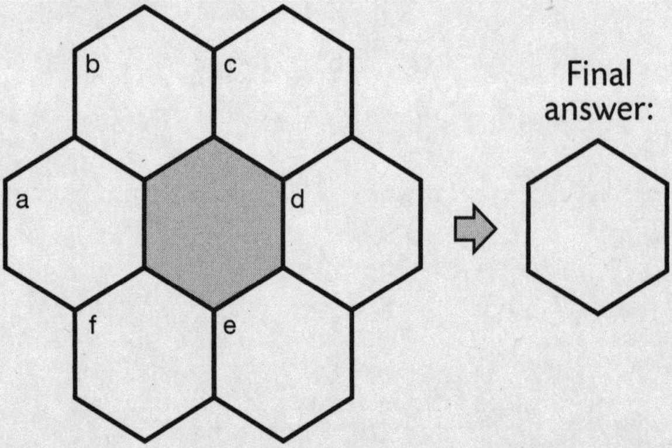

KAKOOMA HARD 6 ADDITION

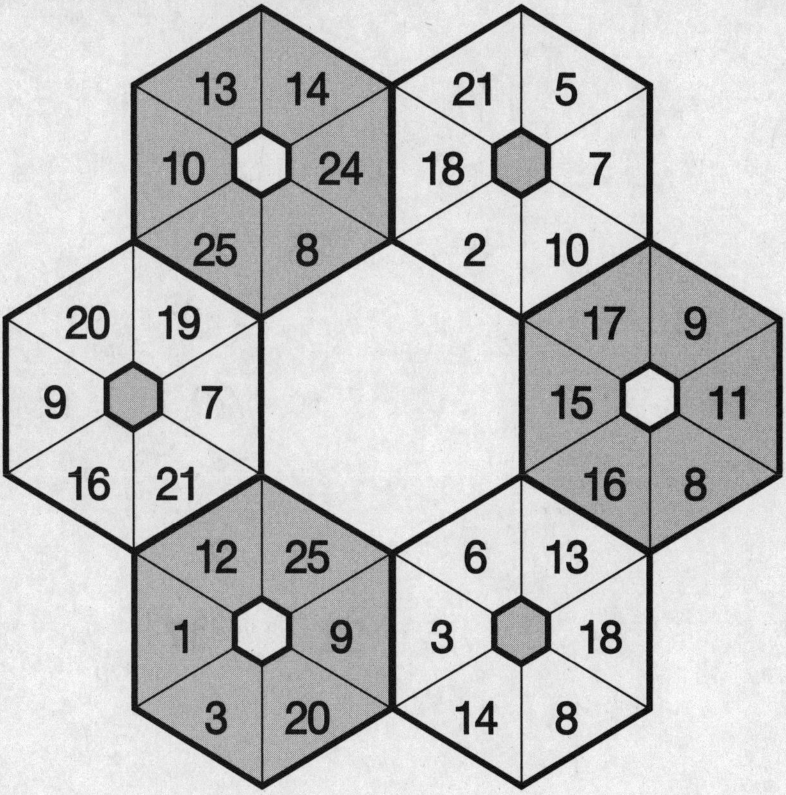

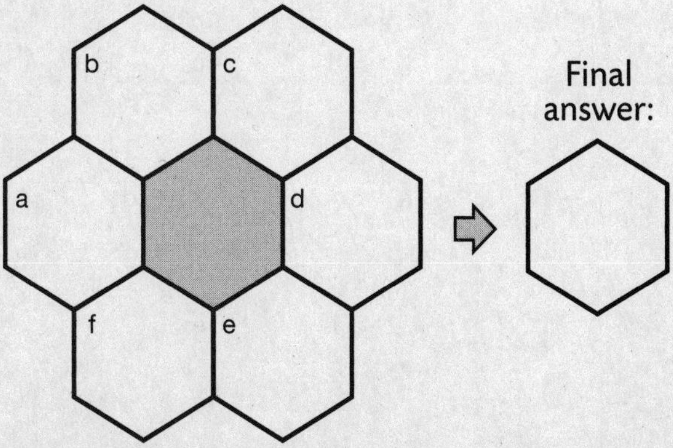

KAKOOMA HARD 6 ADDITION

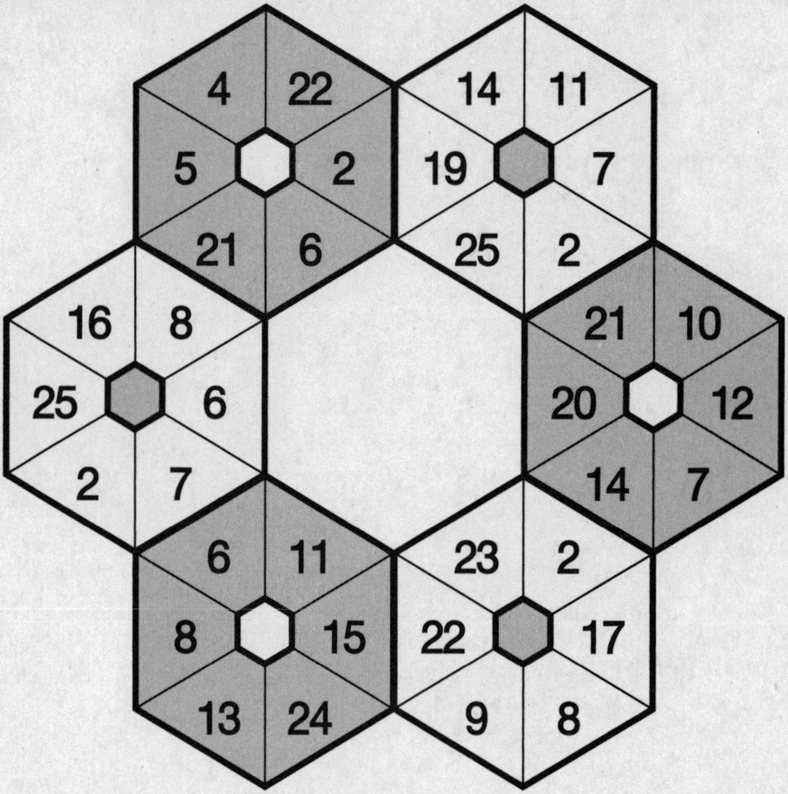

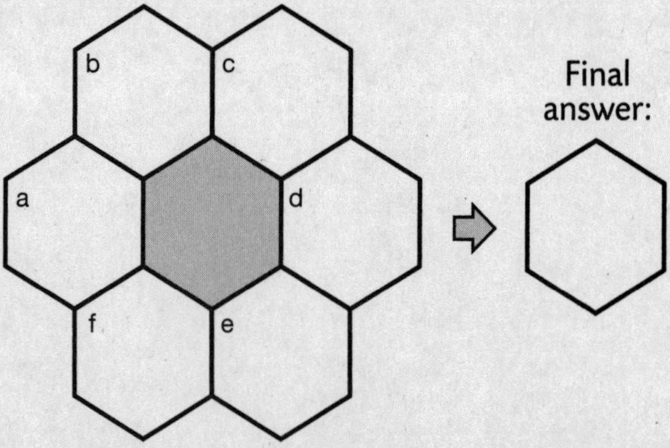

KAKOOMA HARD 6 ADDITION

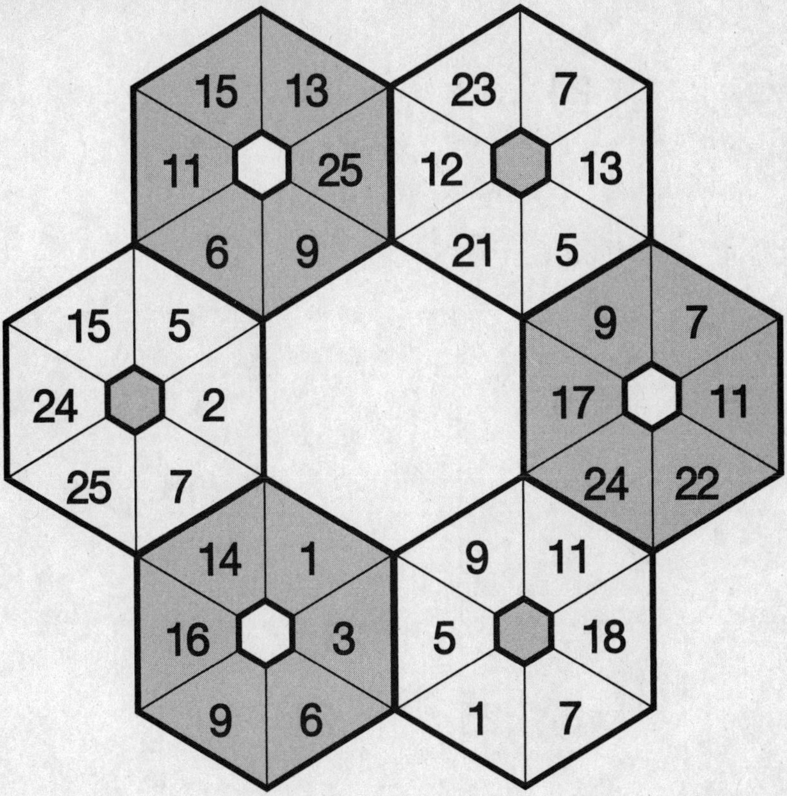

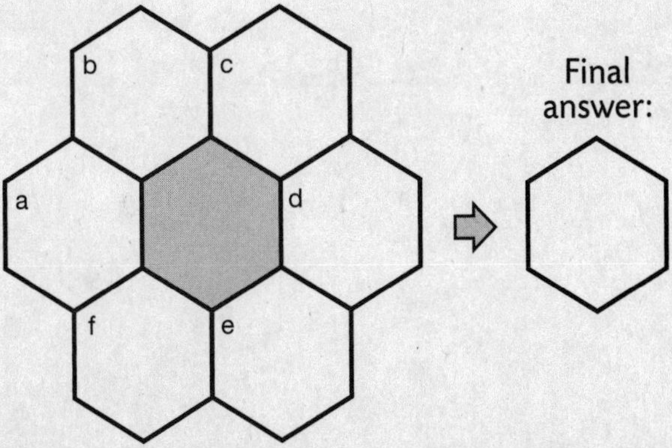

KAKOOMA HARD 6 ADDITION

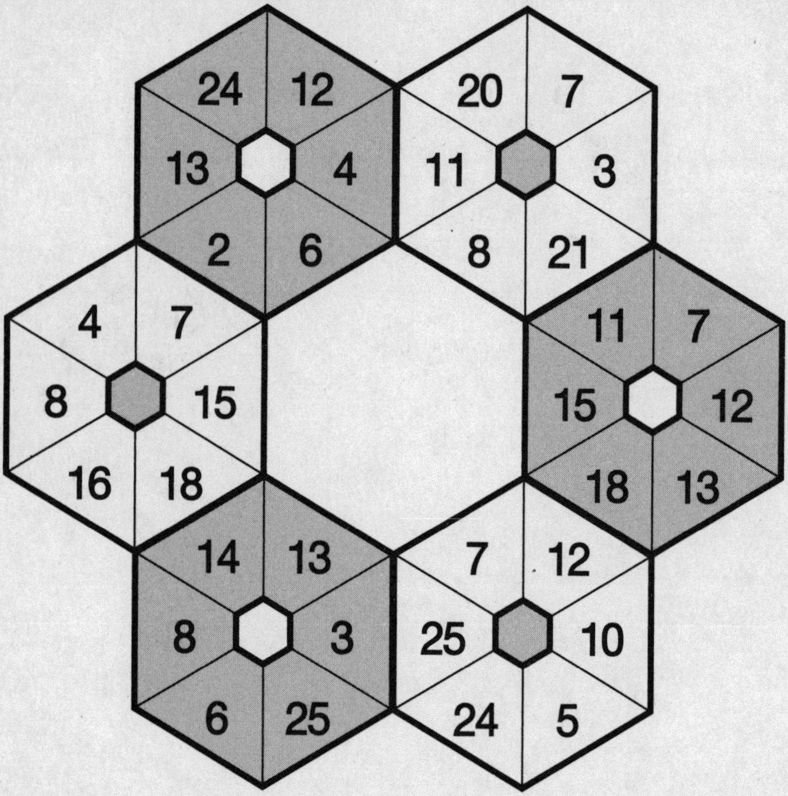

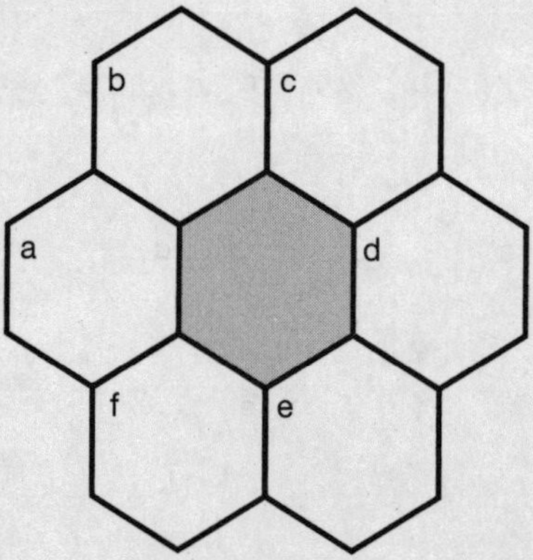

Final answer:

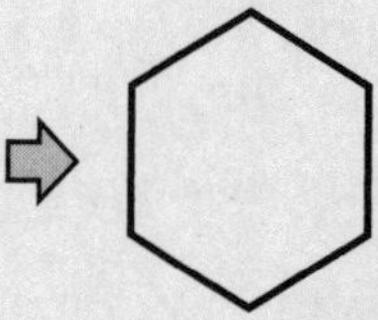

KAKOOMA HARD 6 ADDITION

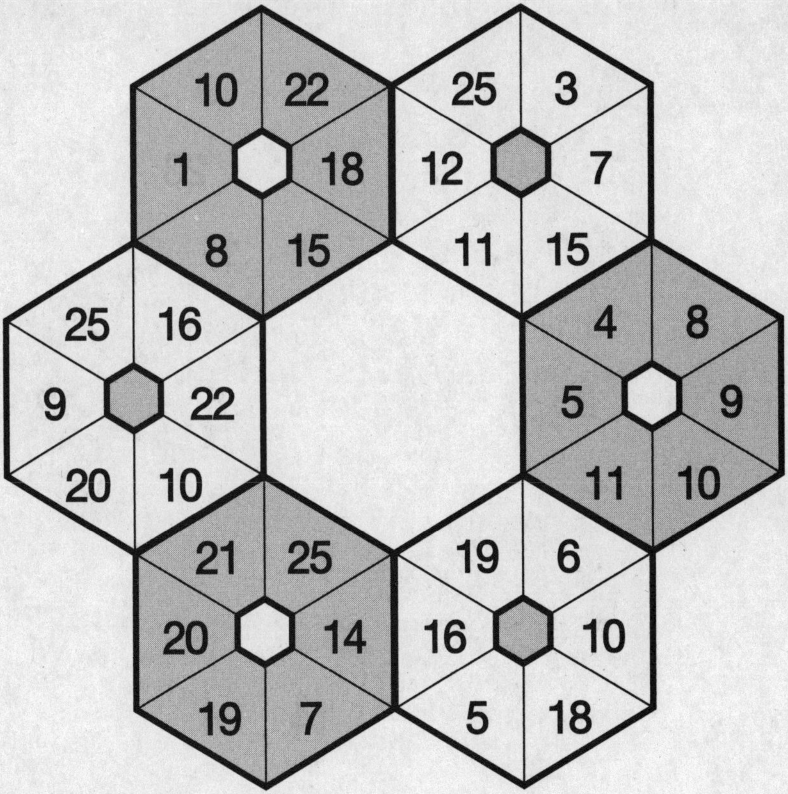

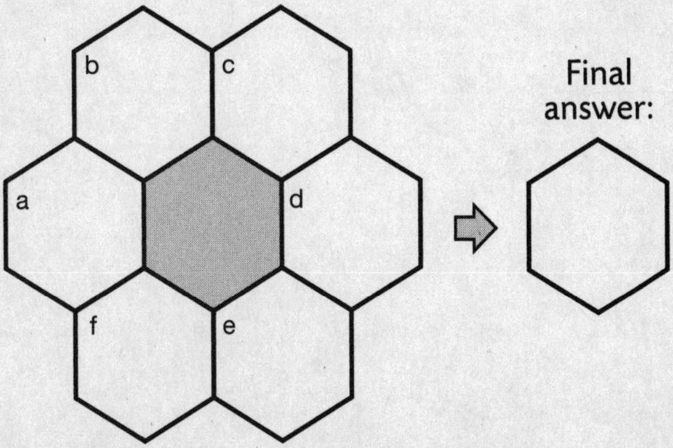

KAKOOMA HARD 6 ADDITION

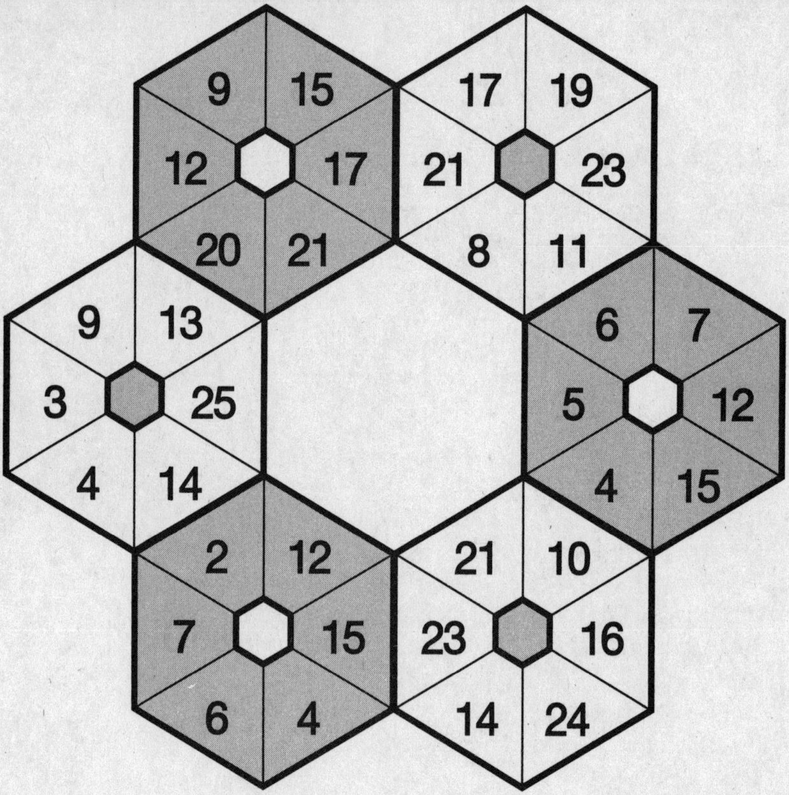

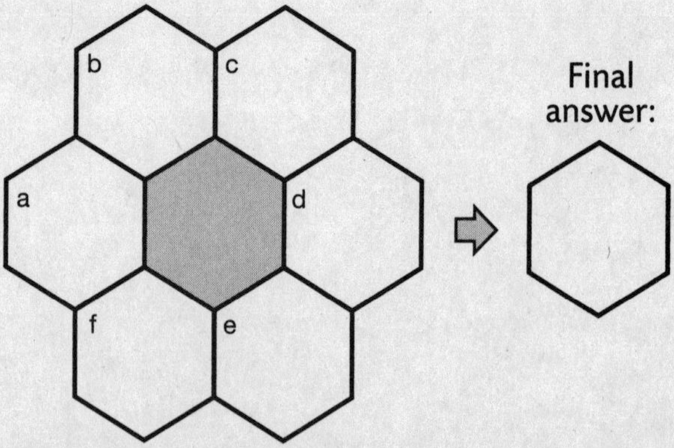

KAKOOMA HARD 6 ADDITION

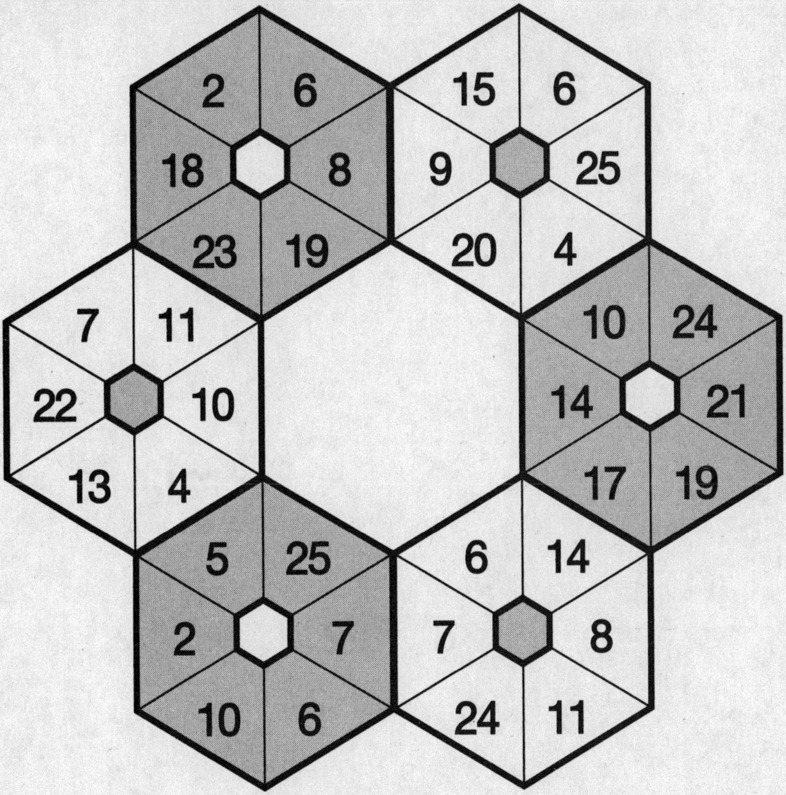

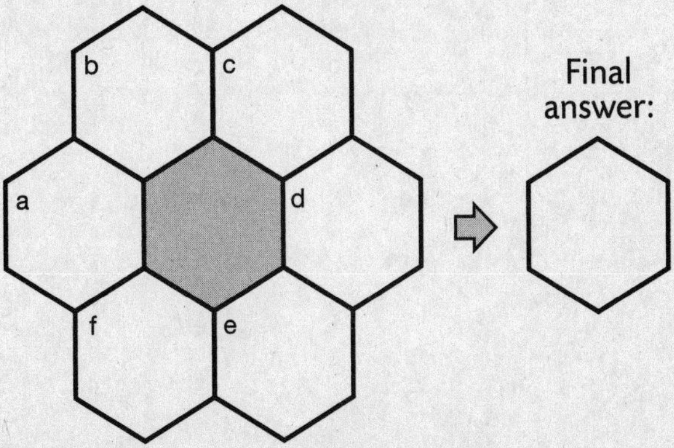

KAKOOMA HARD 6 ADDITION

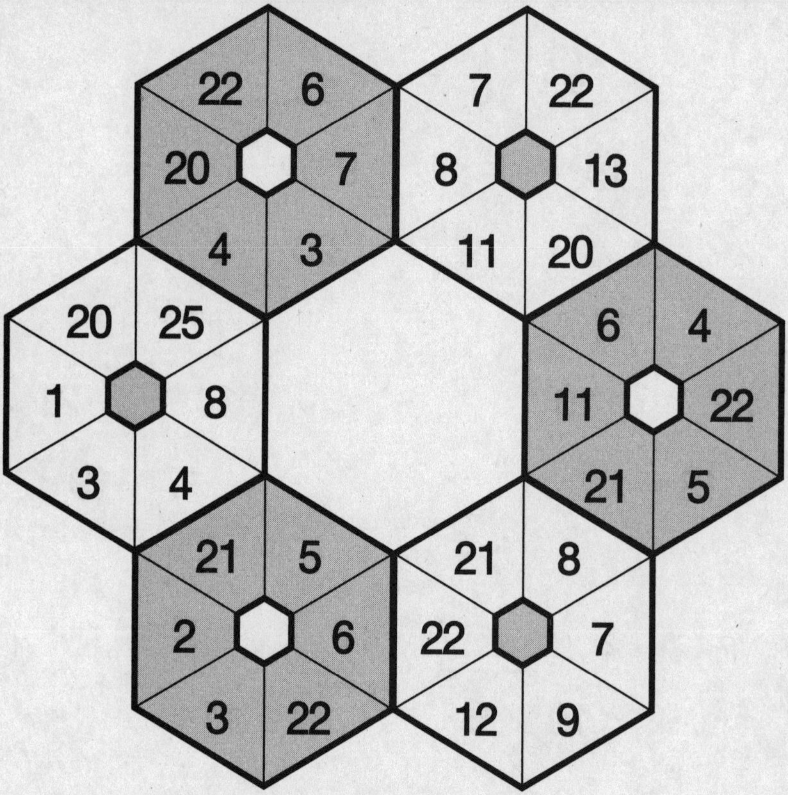

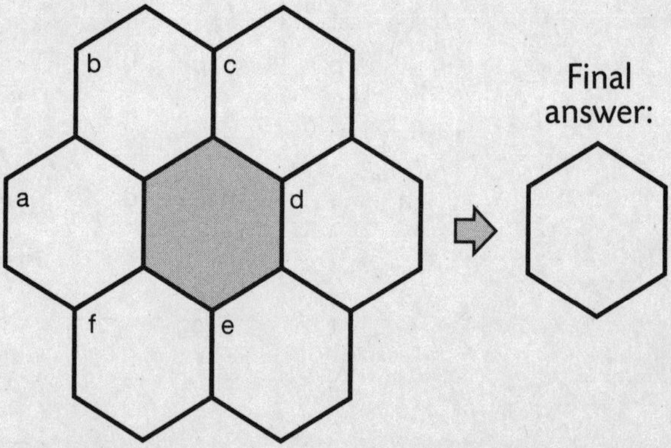

KAKOOMA HARD 6 ADDITION

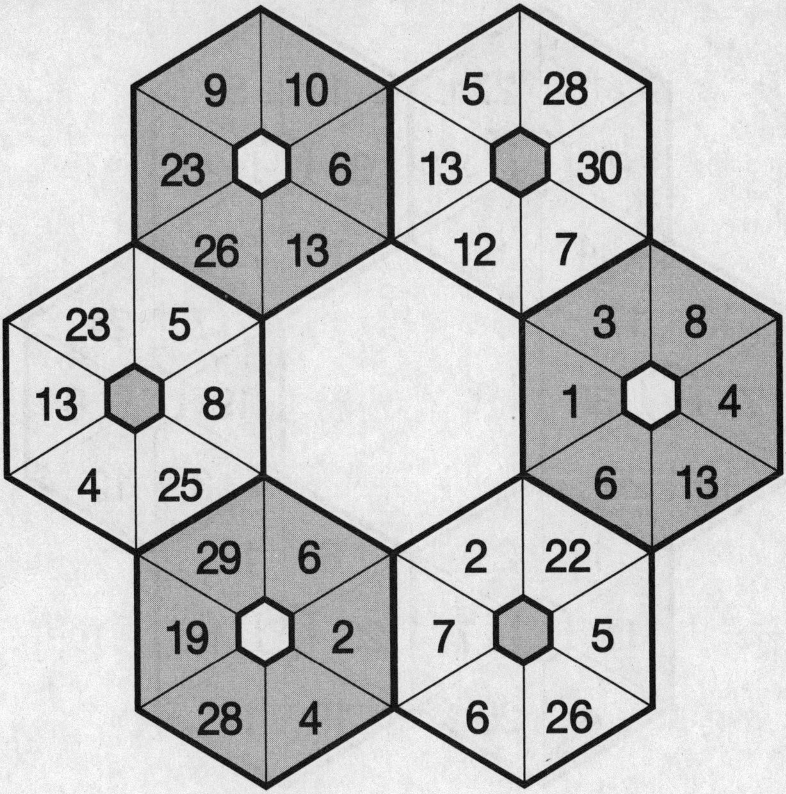

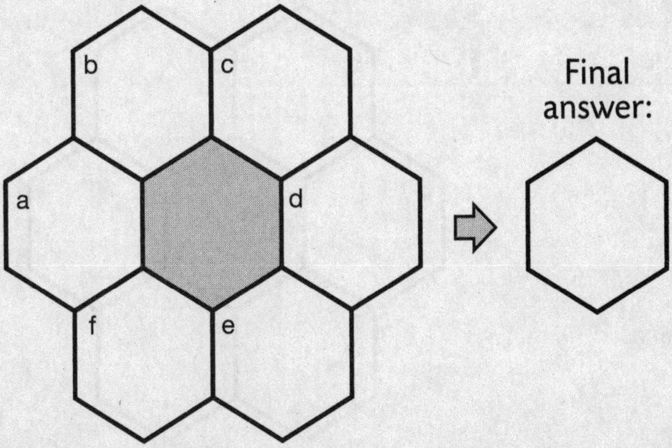

KAKOOMA HARD 6 ADDITION

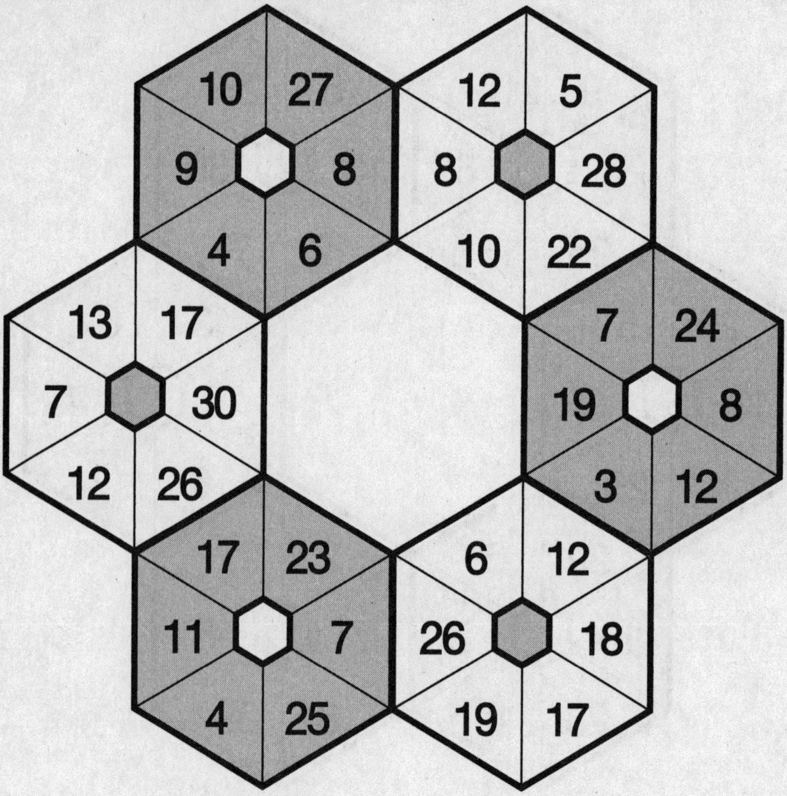

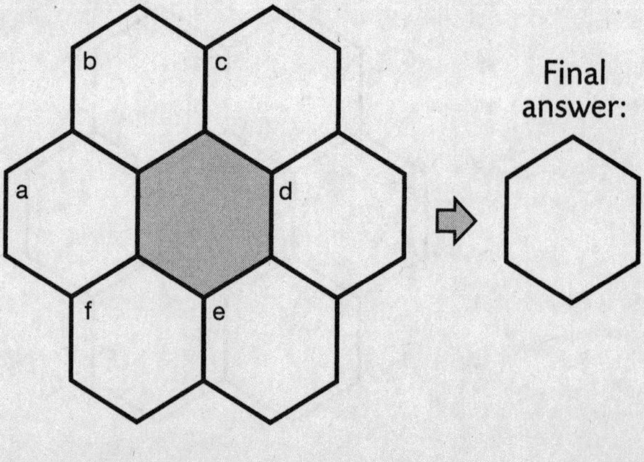

KAKOOMA HARD 6 ADDITION

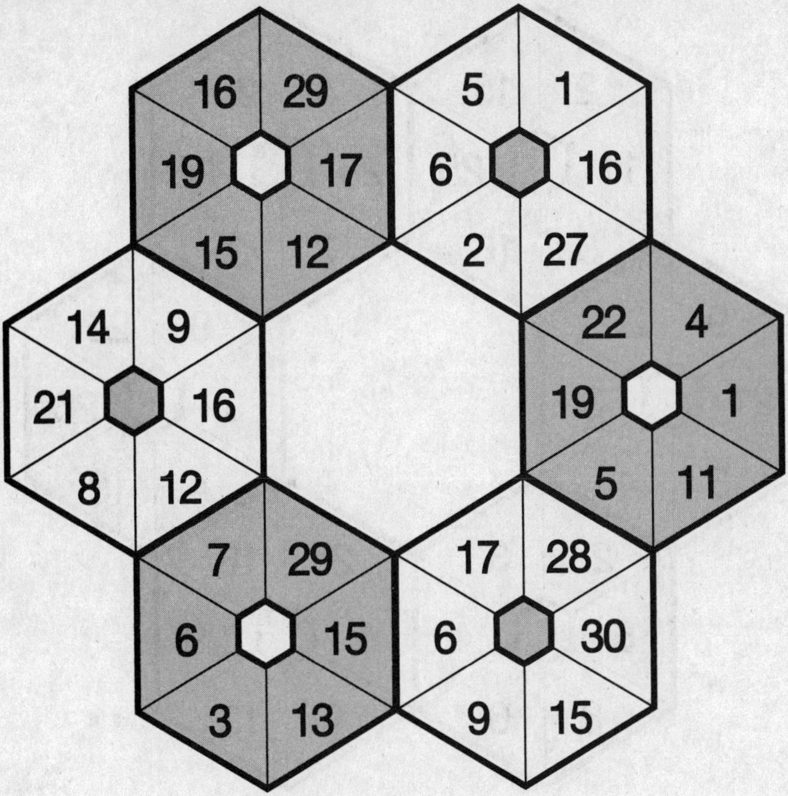

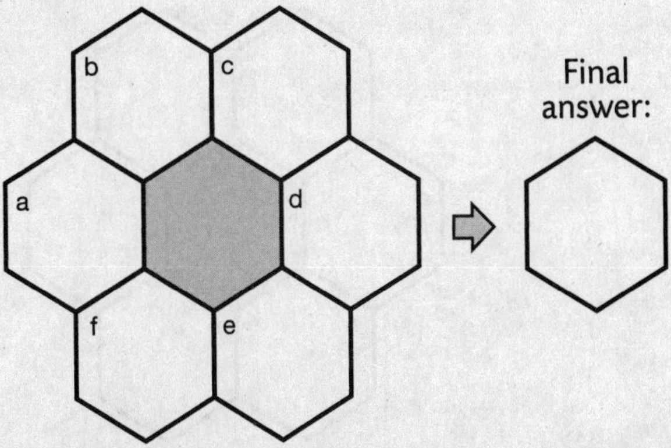

KAKOOMA HARD 6 ADDITION

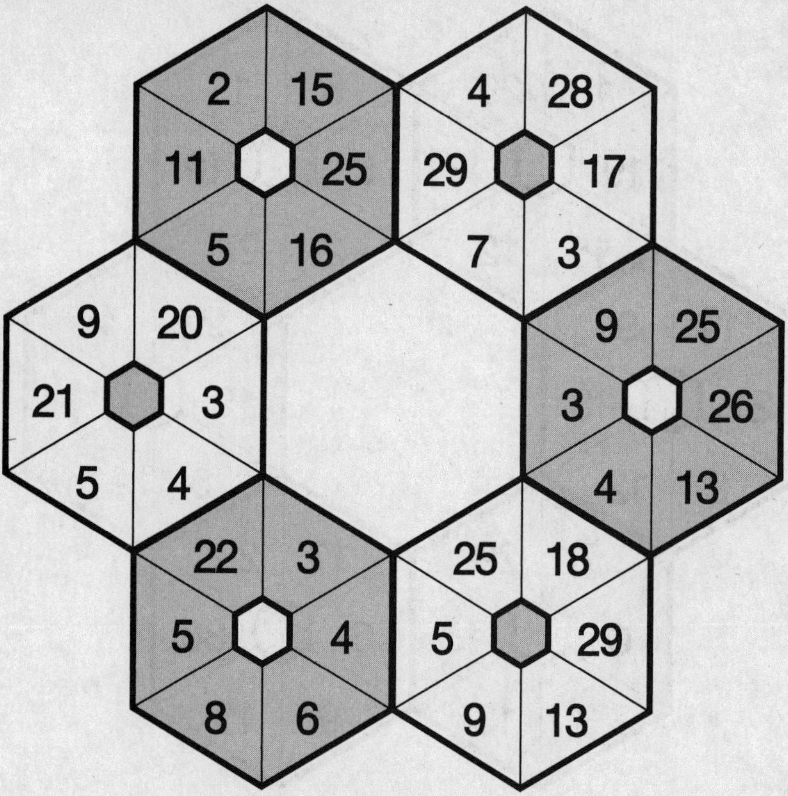

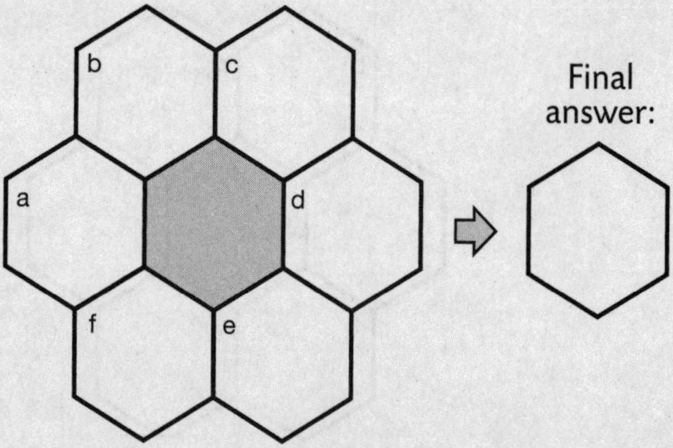

KAKOOMA HARD 6 ADDITION

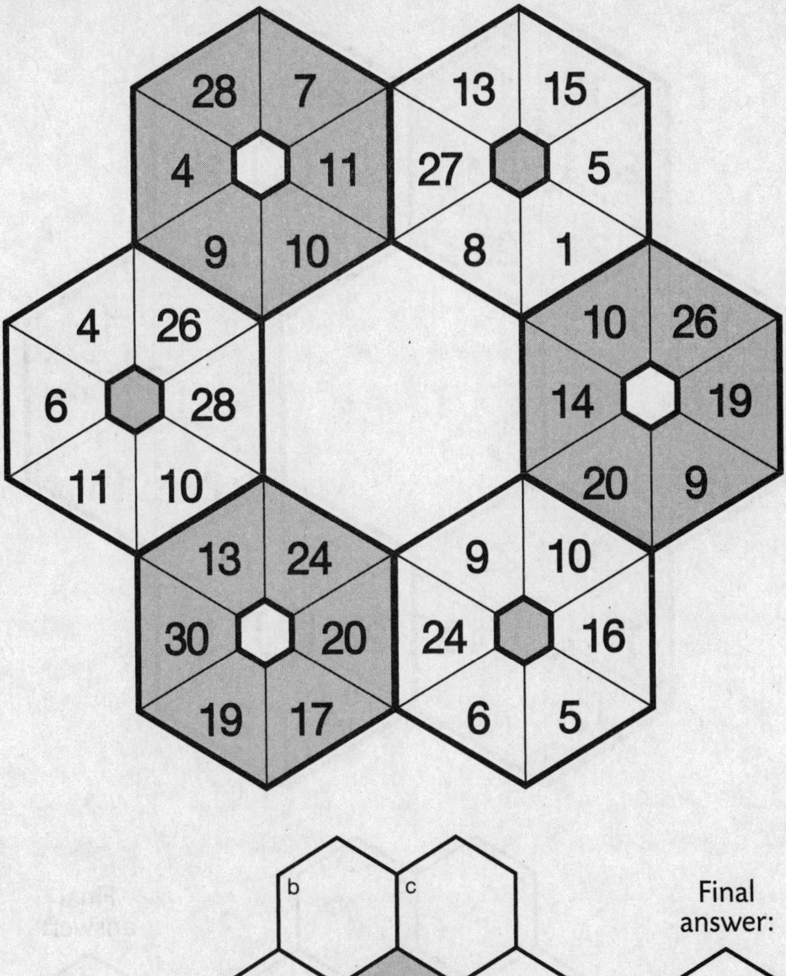

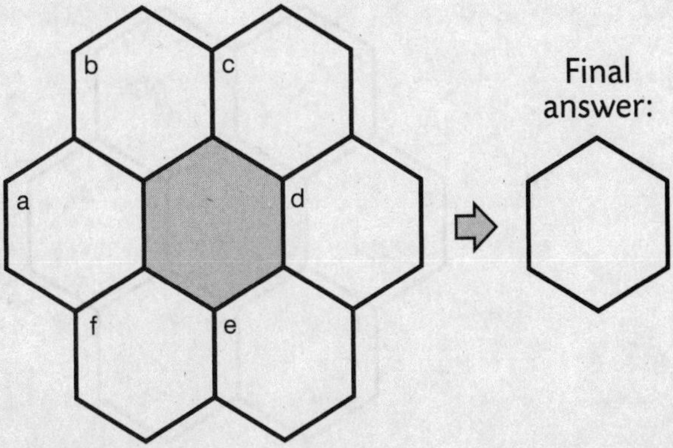

KAKOOMA HARD 6 ADDITION

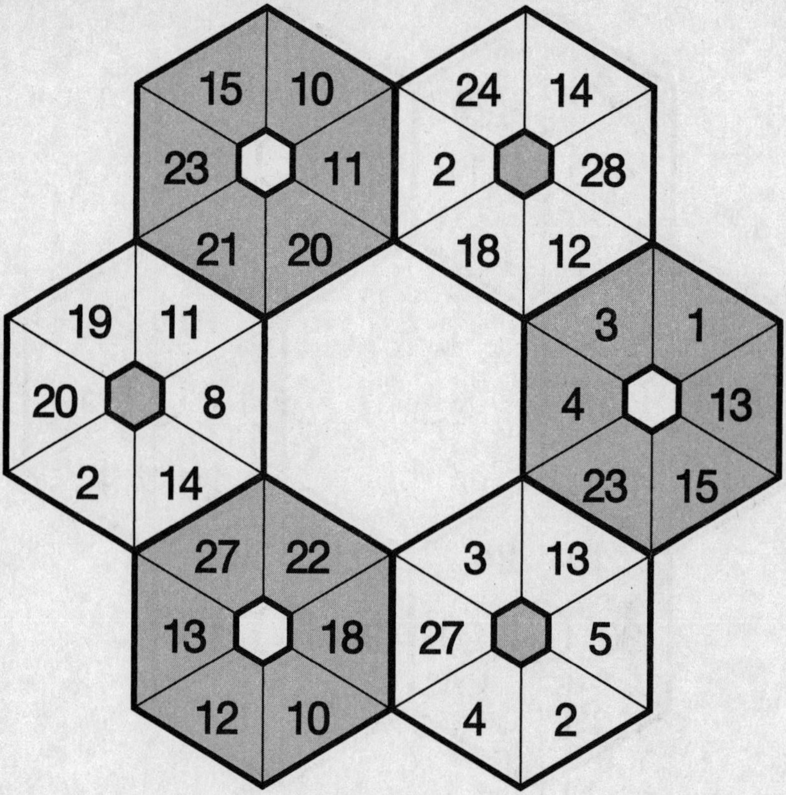

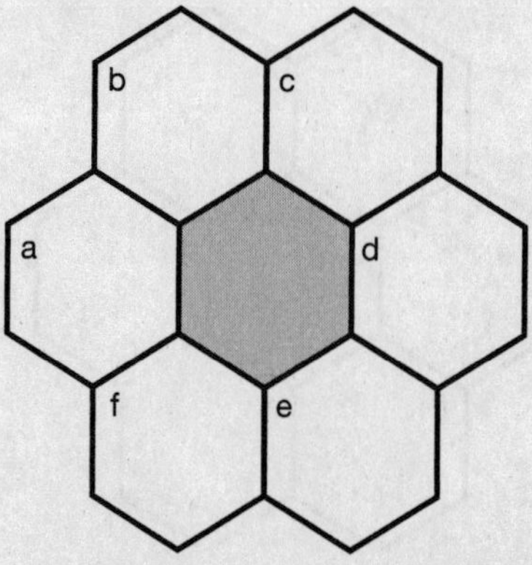

Final answer:

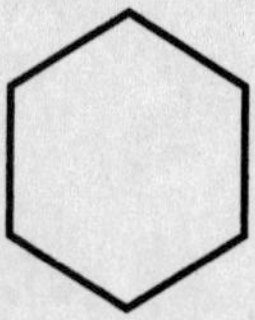

KAKOOMA HARD 6 ADDITION

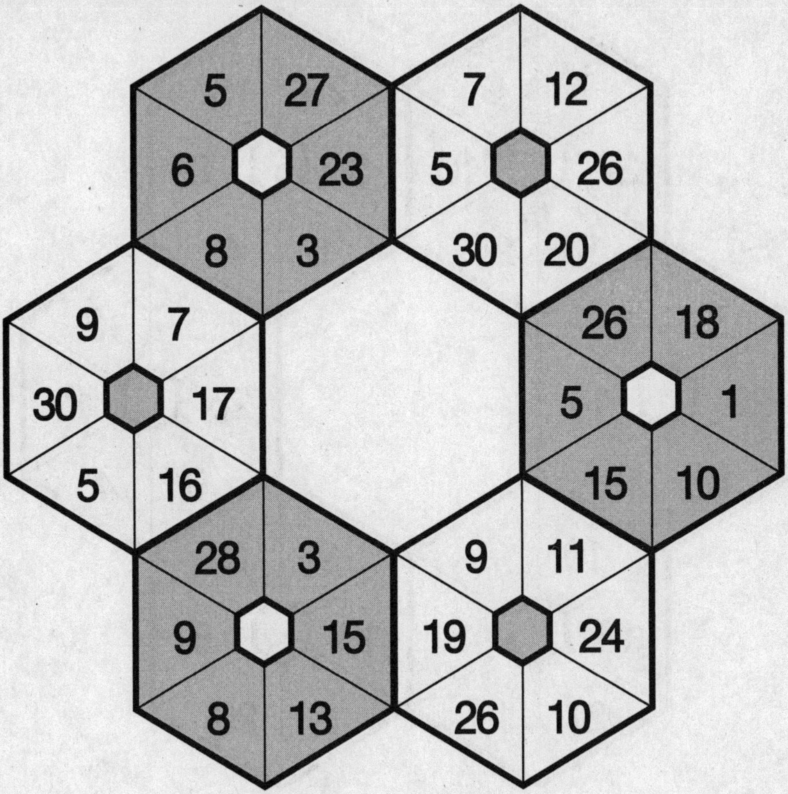

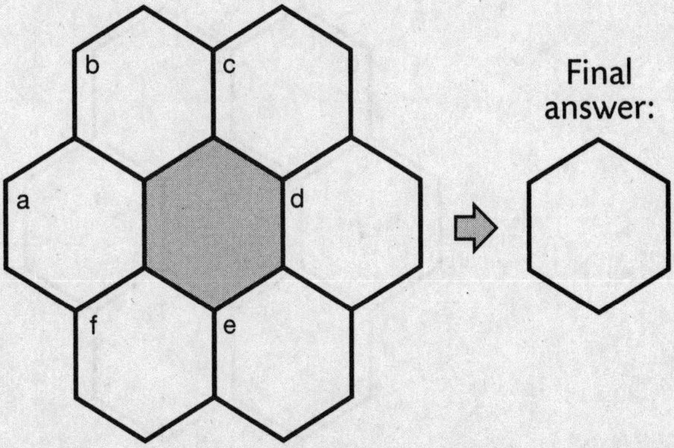

Final answer:

KAKOOMA HARD 6 ADDITION

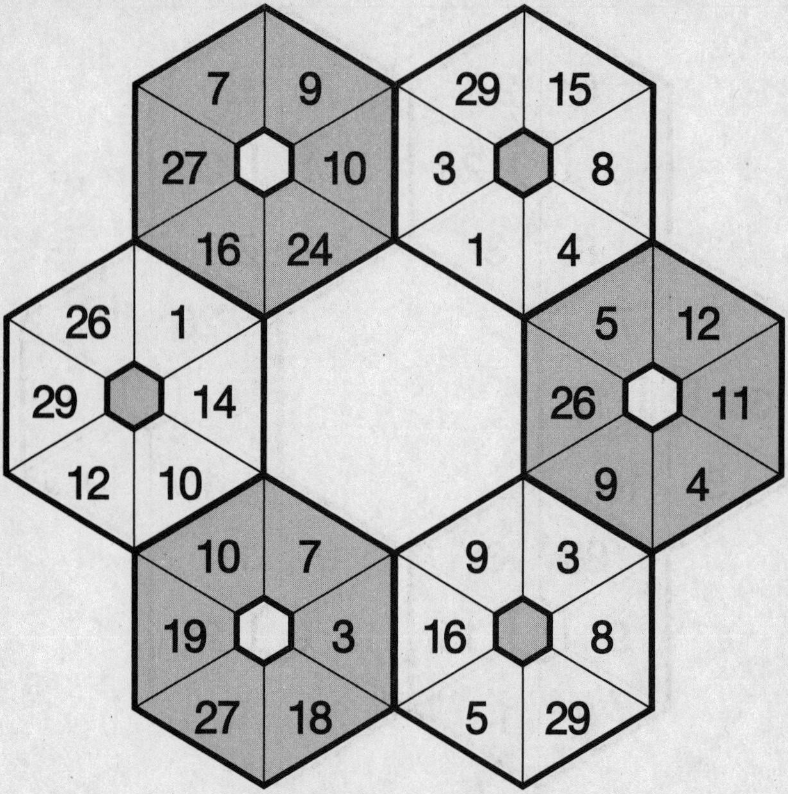

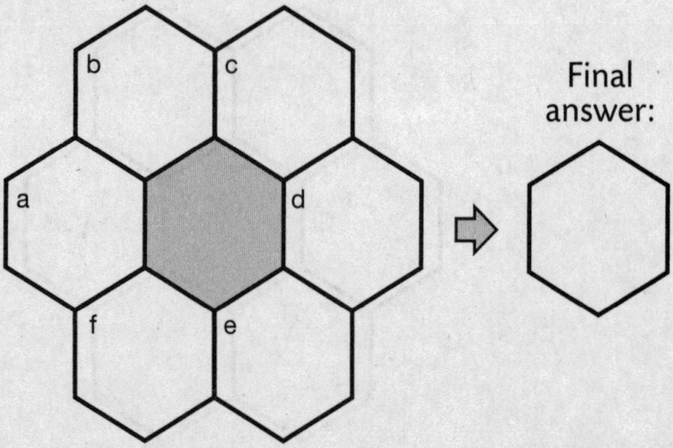

KAKOOMA HARD 6 ADDITION

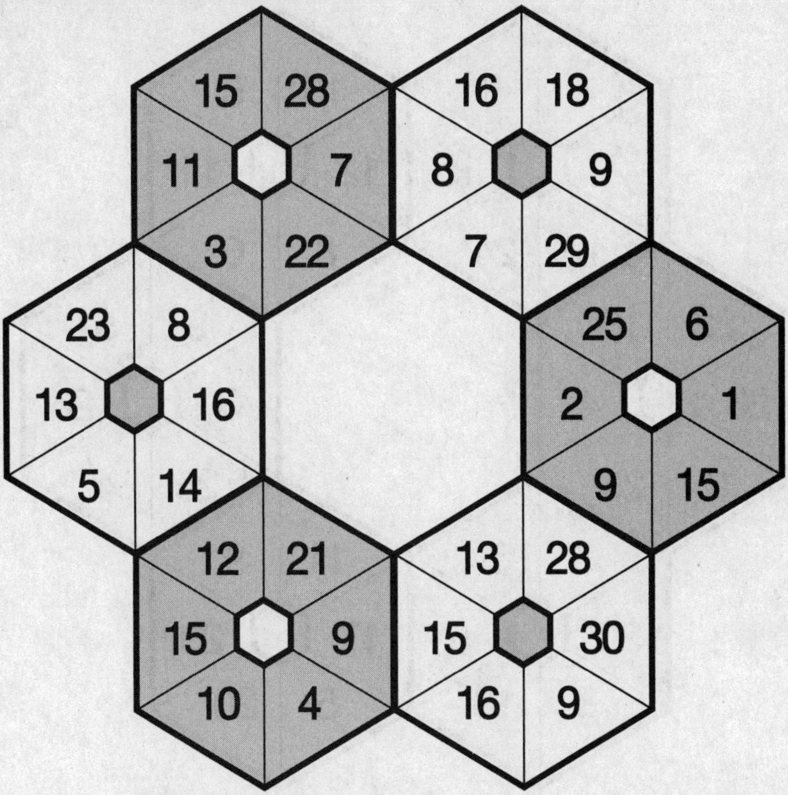

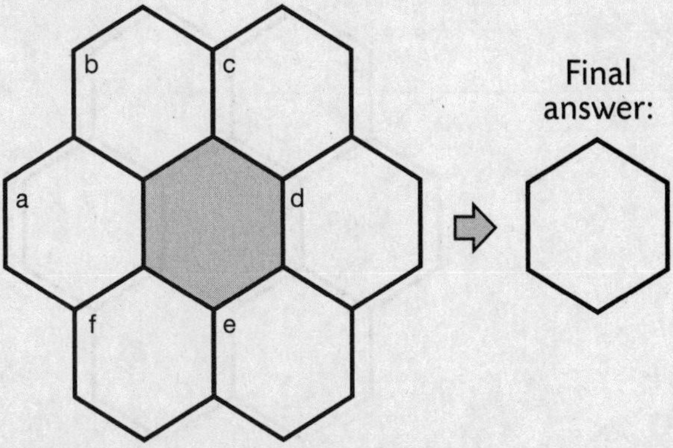

KAKOOMA HARD 6 ADDITION

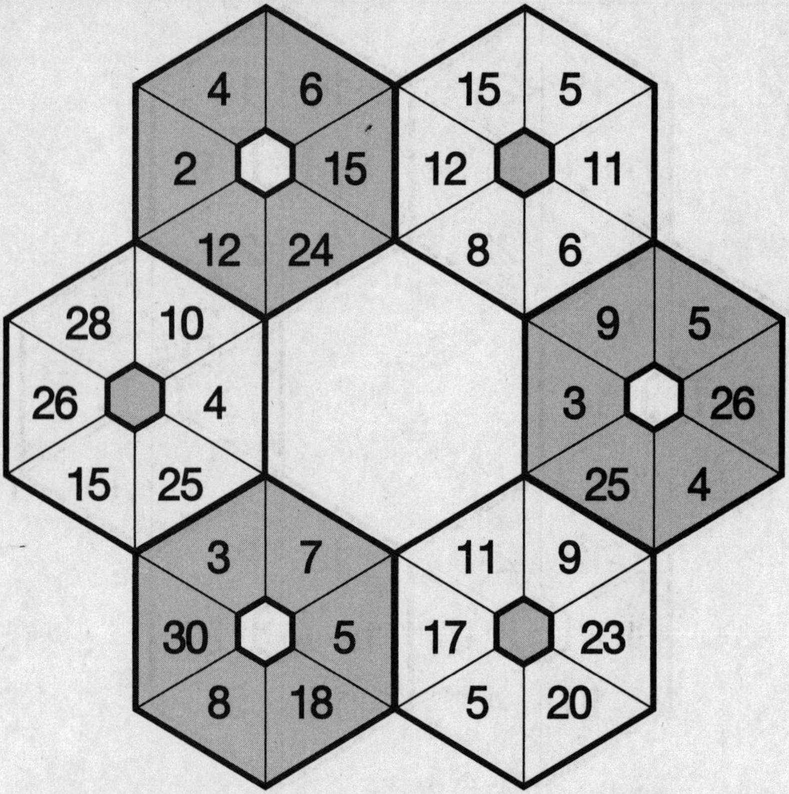

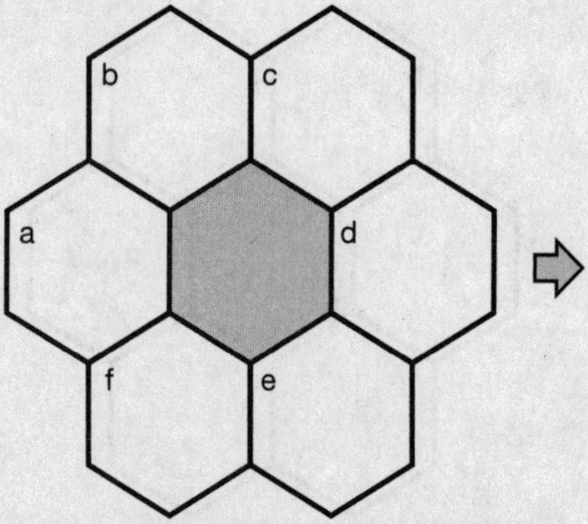

Final answer:

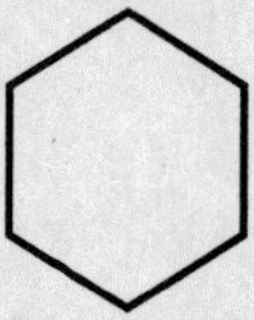

KAKOOMA HARD 6 ADDITION

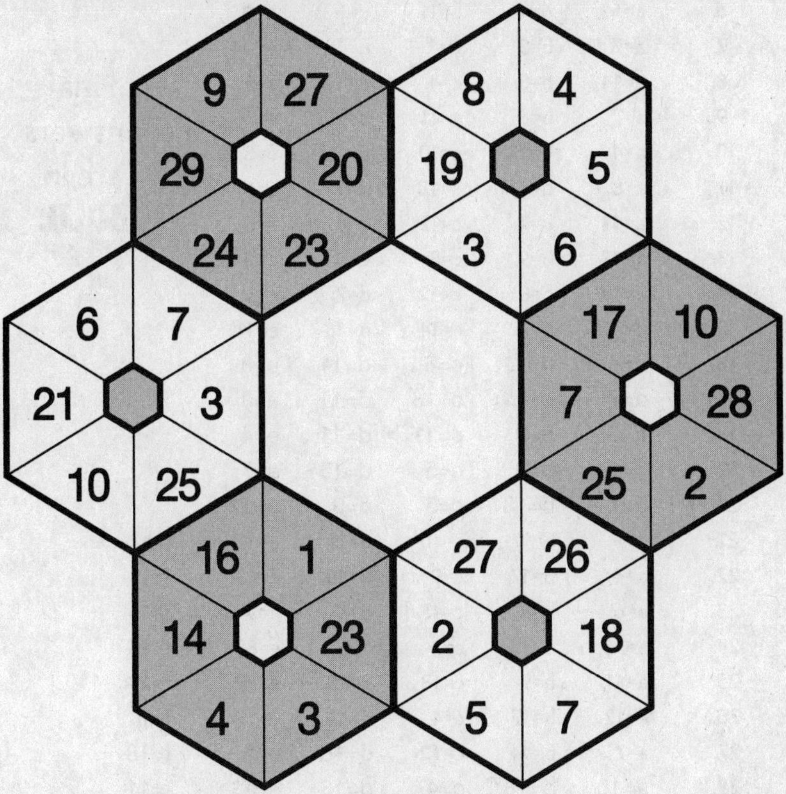

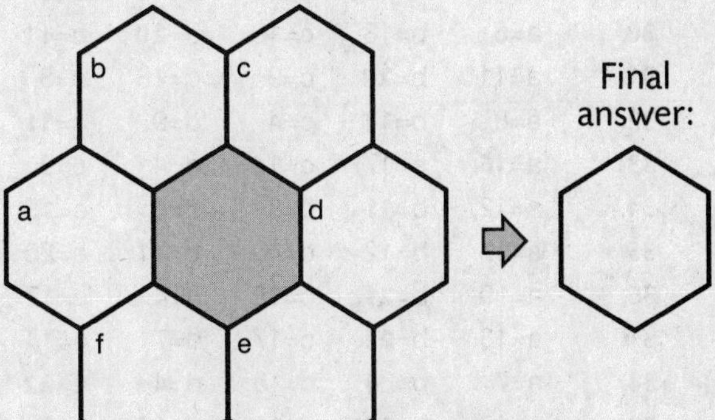

KAKOOMA SOLUTIONS

6.	a=5	b=4	c=11	d=8	e=**9**	
7.	a=7	b=9	c=4	d=10	e=**14**	
8.	a=14	b=8	c=4	d=**13**	e=9	
9.	a=7	b=8	c=11	d=**15**	e=10	
10.	a=4	b=**12**	c=10	d=15	e=8	
11.	a=8	b=11	c=**13**	d=7	e=6	
12.	a=**11**	b=7	c=12	d=4	e=6	
13.	a=**13**	b=9	c=8	d=6	e=5	
14.	a=10	b=8	c=**12**	d=7	e=5	
15.	a=8	b=7	c=14	d=**15**	e=11	
16.	a=4	b=**15**	c=6	d=11	e=8	
17.	a=7	b=**15**	c=13	d=11	e=8	
18.	a=6	b=9	c=**13**	d=11	e=4	
19.	a=**14**	b=9	c=5	d=15	e=7	
20.	a=7	b=13	c=5	d=9	e=**12**	
21.	a=7	b=9	c=10	d=15	e=11	f=**18**
22.	a=4	b=17	c=9	d=**19**	e=15	f=18
23.	a=6	b=8	c=**15**	d=5	e=9	f=16
24.	a=16	b=17	c=7	d=5	e=8	f=**15**
25.	a=11	b=9	c=18	d=19	e=15	f=**20**
26.	a=12	b=17	c=4	d=**15**	e=11	f=18
27.	a=7	b=14	c=**12**	d=16	e=5	f=18
28.	a=10	b=18	c=4	d=13	e=**15**	f=11
29.	a=10	b=12	c=**18**	d=13	e=5	f=4
30.	a=6	b=18	c=16	d=**20**	e=11	f=14
31.	a=11	b=**20**	c=9	d=13	e=8	f=6
32.	a=8	b=14	c=4	d=9	e=**11**	f=7
33.	a=**16**	b=17	c=14	d=4	e=9	f=12
34.	a=12	b=**11**	c=8	d=5	e=15	f=6
35.	a=**17**	b=12	c=4	d=11	e=20	f=5
36.	a=19	b=**21**	c=12	d=4	e=17	
37.	a=13	b=**24**	c=17	d=7	e=14	
38.	a=7	b=24	c=18	d=4	e=**22**	
39.	a=12	b=**23**	c=11	d=16	e=19	
40.	a=23	b=**16**	c=11	d=5	e=24	
41.	a=8	b=**14**	c=23	d=18	e=6	

Final answers are in **BOLD.**

KAKOOMA SOLUTIONS

42.	a=**13**	b=7	c=22	d=6	e=24	
43.	a=6	b=**24**	c=4	d=15	e=20	
44.	a=6	b=9	c=10	d=5	e=**14**	
45.	a=16	b=**25**	c=18	d=7	e=14	
46.	a=6	b=4	c=22	d=20	e=**10**	
47.	a=14	b=15	c=16	d=8	e=**23**	
48.	a=27	b=**30**	c=14	d=16	e=19	
49.	a=15	b=**29**	c=8	d=21	e=10	
50.	a=7	b=13	c=29	d=10	e=**17**	
51.	a=**23**	b=25	c=12	d=11	e=20	
52.	a=7	b=22	c=30	d=11	e=**29**	
53.	a=**12**	b=17	c=4	d=8	e=27	
54.	a=10	b=15	c=**14**	d=4	e=27	
55.	a=4	b=9	c=20	d=14	e=**24**	
56.	a=17	b=6	c=**23**	d=9	e=21	
57.	a=18	b=**24**	c=20	d=11	e=4	f=19
58.	a=19	b=**24**	c=23	d=5	e=9	f=11
59.	a=16	b=**24**	c=7	d=17	e=14	f=12
60.	a=8	b=6	c=**25**	d=21	e=17	f=24
61.	a=7	b=15	c=12	d=**24**	e=18	f=9
62.	a=15	b=6	c=11	d=**18**	e=12	f=14
63.	a=**25**	b=18	c=15	d=9	e=16	f=21
64.	a=13	b=21	c=**19**	d=12	e=24	f=6
65.	a=11	b=8	c=**15**	d=24	e=14	f=7
66.	a=4	b=7	c=20	d=**11**	e=21	f=5
67.	a=**13**	b=23	c=12	d=4	e=7	f=6
68.	a=**30**	b=10	c=22	d=19	e=18	f=11
69.	a=**21**	b=29	c=6	d=5	e=15	f=13
70.	a=9	b=**16**	c=7	d=13	e=18	f=8
71.	a=10	b=11	c=13	d=19	e=16	f=**30**
72.	a=**19**	b=21	c=14	d=4	e=5	f=22
73.	a=16	b=8	c=12	d=15	e=19	f=**28**
74.	a=**26**	b=16	c=4	d=9	e=8	f=10
75.	a=13	b=22	c=16	d=15	e=**28**	f=21
76.	a=25	b=6	c=11	d=9	e=**20**	f=8
77.	a=10	b=29	c=8	d=**17**	e=7	f=4

Congratulations–
I knew I could count
on you to solve all
the puzzles in
this book!
WANT MORE
KAKOOMA?
Log on to www.KAKOOMA.com to:
Access Unlimited Puzzles!
Unlock Challenging New Levels!
Compete Against Kids Across the U.S.!